The Participation Factor

How to Increase Involvement in Occupational Safety

E. Scott Geller

 **AMERICAN SOCIETY OF SAFETY ENGINEERS**

Des Plaines, Illinois   USA

The Participation Factor

Library of Congress Cataloging-in-Publication Data

Geller, E. Scott, 1942–
    The participation factor : how to increase involvement in occupational safety /
    E. Scott Geller.
       p. cm.
    Includes bibliographical references and index.
    ISBN 1-885581-37-8 (pbk. : alk. paper)
      1. Industrial safety--Psychological aspects. 2. Organizational behavior. I. Title.

T55.3.B43 G4488 2002
658.3'82--dc21

2001056569

Published by the American Society of Safety Engineers
1800 E. Oakton Street
Des Plaines, Illinois 60018

This publication is designed to provide accurate and authoritative information in regard to the subject matter covered. It is provided with the understanding that the author is not hereby engaged in rendering legal or other professional services. If legal advice or other professional assistance is required, the services of a competent professional should be sought.

Editor	Sue Knopf, Graffolio
Text Design and Composition	Sue Knopf, Graffolio
Cover Design	Cheryl Reed, Publication Design, Inc.
Managing Editor	Michael F. Burditt, ASSE

Printed in the United States on acid-free paper

2 3 4 5 6 7 8 9

This book is lovingly dedicated to my sister, Suzie,
whose relentless courage and positive attitude
toward participating in life opportunities
overcame forty years of critical physical challenges
caused by systemic lupus erythematosus.

Contents

1

The Three E-Words of Occupational Safety • The Enforcement Approach •
Positive Discipline • Working to Avoid Failure • From a Dependent to an
Interdependent Work Culture

2

You Must Believe • Fear Messages: Scared Safe • Personal Control and
Optimism

3

An Illustrative Anecdote • It's Not Safe to Believe in a Just World • Deciding
Not to Participate • A Consequence Analysis of Participation

4

Participation and Self-Perception • Direct versus Indirect Persuasion •
Self-Directed versus Other-Directed Behavior • Self-Persuasion and Participation

Foreword

Scott Geller's invitation to write the Foreword to his new book—*The Participation Factor*— gives me great pleasure. After meeting Scott in 1991, my career path totally changed. While I was working on culture change at a nuclear site for Virginia Tech, safety became a key issue. Knowing that Scott had been dedicating most of his research and teaching to the human dynamics of safety, I asked for his help, but received a lot more.

For almost ten years now, I've been working with Scott to teach and implement the principles and procedures described in this book. As a safety consultant, one of my greatest challenges has been to increase and maintain participation in the various safety-related activities of behavior-based safety. So, I was pleased when Scott decided to incorporate his years of experience and expertise in a book about increasing involvement in occupational safety.

Scott's writing is consistently lucid, straightforward, and easy to understand. His use of personal stories and graphic illustrations not only keeps you entertained, but also helps you remember the principles and procedures. All of these are founded on rigorous research and are instrumental in getting more people engaged in efforts to prevent workplace injuries. You'll learn how to put an achievement focus on safety; how to support and sustain active involvement through one-on-one conversation; how to bring out the best in people with effective leadership and positive reinforcement; how to help people transition from being held accountable to feeling responsible for safety; how to fuel participation with principles of social influence; how to develop interpersonal trust throughout a work culture; how to use the competence motive to make safety a value rather than a priority; and how to build and maintain momentum for your safety process.

Who should read *The Participation Factor*? The lessons in this book are directly relevant for anyone who wants to prevent unintentional injuries in the workplace. However, the principles in this book are universally applicable. They can be used in any situation that depends on the actively caring contributions of people–whether performing at home, at work, in school, on the athletic field, or in the community at large.

Over the years since I've known Scott, he never seems to lose his extraordinary enthusiasm, drive, and passion to truly make a difference in people's lives–from the university classroom to the organizational setting. My friendship and professional partnership with Scott has changed my life's goals and mission. I look forward to continuing our collaborative activities at Safety Performance Solutions and thereby continuously improve as a safety professional, as well as an actively caring citizen of the United States of America. Don't delay, read this book today to fuel *The Participation Factor* in your organization.

Anne R. French, Ph.D.
Senior Partner
Safety Performance Solutions

Preface

Imagine trying to get someone to participate in an activity that does not provide soon and certain payoffs—only the promise that an aversive consequence could be avoided. But, daily experience suggests the activity is really unnecessary because nonparticipation does not result in a negative consequence. Imagine also that nonparticipation is actually rewarded with such soon and certain consequences as greater efficiency, convenience, comfort—and sometimes peer approval.

I'm sure you realize I'm talking about safety, and the special challenge of getting people involved in taking the time to do a variety of things that could prevent an injury—from analyzing near hits* and property-damage incidents to conducting environmental and behavioral audits and implementing follow-up corrective-action plans. But that's not all.

Now imagine that past attempts to improve participation in safety-related activities have been confrontational, insulting, and even humiliating. I'm referring to the traditional "command-and-control" approach to safety that delivers its "call for participation" with such words as "regulation," "government standard," "mandatory compliance," "accident investigation," and "occupant restraint"; and uses slogans like "Safety is a condition of employment," and "All accidents are preventable." And I'm not done yet.

Consider also that historically, most safety matters have been handled by a select number of employees, often by one person—the company "safety director." These few individuals, typically called safety professionals, attend safety conferences, communicate with corporate leaders and government agencies about safety issues, investigate accidents, calculate injury statistics,

---

* "Near hit" is used throughout this text instead of the more common term "near miss" because a literal translation of near miss would mean the injury actually occurred.

manage lost-time cases, coordinate safety training sessions, and assume the leadership role at all important safety meetings. Furthermore, only these individuals have the education and experience to interpret the thick government rule books on safety standards.

Imagine all of this and you'll see why getting more participation in safety is so difficult. We need to overcome prejudice from past experience, contrary perceptions, attitudes and behavioral contingencies in the current work culture, and natural resistance to change familiar and convenient routines for the uncertainties of a new process or procedure.

Then there's the problem of selecting an alternative approach to occupational safety. It's rational to be skeptical about whom to listen to and what to do. Safety suffers from the "flavor-of-the-month" syndrome, perhaps more than any other field. Of course, I'm referring only to the human dynamics of injury prevention. Engineers and industrial hygienists can advise us quite precisely on how to make equipment, work stations, and the atmosphere safer. Why? Because these disciplines have a history of rigorous research to consult. This is not the case for the human dynamics of safety.

The science of psychology is less than 150 years old, and only within the last 50 years has psychological research addressed safety issues. In fact, the application of psychological research to improve safety performance started with some fervor only in the early 1990s, with the emergence of behavior-based safety. Even though the principles and methods of behavior-based safety are based on research, however, there is much confusion and controversy about this approach. Some claim a focus on work practices takes attention away from engineering and hygiene intervention (Foster 2000; Howe 1998; Hoyle 1998) while others advocate a broader and more holistic human focus on perceptions, attitudes, and culture (Petersen 2001; Simon 2001; Topf 2001).

So even when systematic research demonstrates significant success for a particular approach toward addressing the human aspects of occupational safety (as reviewed in Geller 2001d; Petersen 1989; Sulzer-Azaroff, McCann, and Harris 2001), misunderstanding and controversy surface. Some of this is legitimate skepticism, but some is merely a consultant's attempt to attract business. I discuss these issues of discord and confusion about behavior-based safety elsewhere (Geller 1999, 2001f). Here I only want to make the point that deciding how to address the human dynamics of occupational safety can be quite challenging. Relevant research on the subject is rare, and the most rigorous research available is frequently misinterpreted, misunderstood, and sometimes misapplied.

With a lack of clear research answers to questions about the human dynamics of safety, safety professionals rely on pop psychology to address the people part of their jobs. How do I know? Over the years I've attended countless conference presentations related to the psychology of safety, listened to more than a hundred self-help audiotapes, and read numerous books and articles by authors who write about the psychology of safety but have minimal formal education in psychology.

When these speakers or authors actually reference their assertions about some psychological principle—a rare occurrence—they hardly ever cite research. Instead, they refer to pop psychology books, some of which have no research foundation or present a narrow or misguided view of the research literature. Many safety speakers and authors don't even attempt to seek verification of their psychological dialogue from other sources. Some actually proclaim that dealing with the human aspects of safety requires only "good common sense."

Elsewhere (Geller 2001d), I debunk pop psychology and common sense as sources for answers to questions about the human dynamics of safety. Here, I use this issue to corroborate further the special difficulties one should expect when addressing the human side of safety—especially the crucial and challenging mission of increasing the quality and quantity of employee involvement in occupational safety. I call this *The Participation Factor.*

This book is about fueling *The Participation Factor* of occupational safety in order to achieve an ultimate vision: an injury-free workplace. The principles and procedures given here are not taken from pop psychology, nor are they based on common sense. Rather, rigorous psychological research is used to support the advice I offer for activating and sustaining safety participation. Key sources for the supportive research are given, as well as the more readable reviews of the relevant literature.

In addition to research verification, I had hoped to include industry-based examples of various participation principles and procedures. To make this happen, I mailed this book's prospectus and two related papers to more than one hundred safety leaders along with an invitation to submit real-world anecdotes to exemplify any of the participation principles described. Although many of the recipients told me they would send me a participation story, I received relevant information from only one person—Shane Pourciau, the Safety Supervisor of Cajun Constructors Piling Division, headquartered in Baton Rouge, Louisiana.

Shane's story, complete with procedural details, photographs, and outcome data, is an awe-inspiring demonstration of applying the principles of employee empowerment presented in Chapter 2 of this book. However, rather than present this single illustration of fueling *The Participation Factor,* I've decided to solicit more organizational applications of the strategies described in this book, with hopes of including a variety of examples in a subsequent edition. Thus, I ask every reader to look for demonstrations of the techniques I offer here for increasing employee involvement in occupational safety, and then to please send me information we can use in the next edition of this book to inspire others to energize *The Participation Factor* in their organizations.

I expect some readers will find many principles and procedures presented here to be consistent with their own common sense and with messages they receive from pop psychologists and motivational speakers. That's a good sign. It reflects education and experience consistent with objective evidence. Please realize, however, that much of what is commonly done to increase safety participation is not consistent with the research literature—nor are these standard approaches very effective.

Thus, the "common sense" practiced regularly to get people involved in occupational safety is not consistent with many recommendations given in this book. I sincerely hope the lessons here will inform and improve the common sense of the safety profession. But this can only happen if you—the reader—learn these lessons and teach them to others.

With the help of George Wills, I've included a number of original cartoons to illuminate various points and make the learning process fun. I've added these illustrations in spite of one reviewer's advice that "cartoons are not needed as much in a book as they are in a presentation, [and] buyers may be dissatisfied if there is too much space devoted to them." I hope you find the cartoons useful and enjoyable. More importantly, I hope this book activates you to teach the principles and procedures exemplified in both the text and the illustrations. Please feel free to photocopy and enlarge the figures for your own presentations. I ask only that you tell people where you got them.

My mission is to inspire you to teach and implement the practical procedures in this book. When you do, you will fuel *The Participation Factor* and prevent personal injuries. Together we will make a difference!

E. Scott Geller
January 2002

Acknowledgments

I'm proud to acknowledge this book as containing more generally applicable information about the human dynamics of safety than any other book currently available. This statement is not as bold and risky as it might seem. The most practical books addressing human aspects of occupational safety are those focusing on behavior-based safety, and these are pertinent for fewer circumstances than those serviced by *The Participation Factor*. The principles and procedures in this book are applicable to any safety-related activity that benefits from more input or involvement from people.

Why start my acknowledgments with an affirmation of the widespread pragmatic value of this book? Well, the fact is, I could not have gained the knowledge and inspiration to write this book without an incredible amount of support and guidance from significant others. Textbooks, research reports, and university colleagues taught me the relevant psychological principles; and thirty years of interacting with industrial employees shaped my perspectives and recommendations for realistic applications. Plus, the passionate desire to make a difference that is so prominent among the safety leaders I've met motivated me to write this text. I am deeply grateful for the invaluable instruction, insight, and inspiration I've received from these countless contacts and relationships.

I can pinpoint five support systems that made this publication possible, and I'd like to identify each. First, my immediate family—Carol, Betty, Krista, and Karly—who care for my basic needs, motivate me to achieve, and have put up with my endless and unfair substitution of "professional time" for "family time."

Second, my students and associates in our university Center for Applied Behavior Systems who collect and analyze endless streams of field data to test the effects of various participation factors and inform the design of more effective procedures for increasing involvement in safety-related activities. This support system also serves as a "think tank" for considering innovative approaches to understanding and influencing the human dynamics of safety and for developing research procedures to analyze the impact of variables that could affect *The Participation Factor.* In this regard, I am particularly beholden to my current graduate students, including Chris Dula, Kelli Will, Angela Fournier, Jeff Hickman, and Phil Lehman, the Center coordinator, Ian Ehrhart, and the Center's research scientist, Kent Glindemann. Ian Ehrhart merits special recognition and gratitude because he word-processed the entire text for this book from my handwritten drafts and prepared the electronic files for all the figures and illustrations. Thank you, Ian—I could not have done this without your invaluable talent and dedication.

My colleagues at Safety Performance Solutions (SPS) represent a third support system that made this book possible. For almost a decade, this leading-edge training and consulting firm has taught organizations how to improve their safety culture and prevent personal injuries by applying the human dynamics revealed in this book. By working closely with the leaders of this group, especially Susan "Bix" Bixler, Anne French, Mike Gilmore, Molly McClintock, Sherry Perdue, Chuck Pettinger, Steve Roberts, and Josh Williams, I have developed meaningful empirical questions for programmatic research, learned how to make our research findings more applicable to industrial safety, and gained insight for teaching others the most relevant implications of our research. As such, SPS represents the extension agent of our university research center and turns our vision to make a difference into reality.

The fourth essential support system includes the individuals I have worked with directly to make this book a reality. Specifically, the editorial talents and design skills of Sue Knopf resulted in clearer prose and an attractive and interesting page layout, and the graphic artistry of Cheryl Reed of Publication Design, Inc. resulted in an eye-catching cover. George Wills drew all the illustrations, usually from only my general verbal description of what I wanted to portray. The publication department of the American Society of Safety Engineers, especially Michael Burditt and Chuck Coffin, gave me critical support throughout the entire publication process. They believed in my initial vision, organized a committee review and evaluation of my prospectus, and then planned and coordinated the editing, printing, distributing and marketing of *The Participation Factor.*

Finally, I want to recognize and genuinely thank the many individuals who taught me the valuable lessons reflected in this book and inspired me to teach these lessons to others. I can honestly say there are too many of these individuals to mention here. And if I did try to list them, my memory would fail me and I'd miss many. But, that's a cop-out. The following is a list of those people worldwide whose interactions with me guided my research and scholarship, challenged me to improve the link between research and application, and fueled my own *Participation Factor* for this project. Yes, I have missed many significant persons. If your name is missing from this list, please accept my apology and sincere appreciation for contributing to my learning and motivation.

Those of you whom I remember today—Gary Arcus, Diana Ash, John Austin, Nate Azrin, Ed Baber, Don Baer, Jon Bailey, James Banner, Scott Barker, Rick Bennett, Tom Berry, Bruce Bigelow, Frank Bird, Earl Blair, Ken Blanchard, Dwight Blankenbaker, David Blyth, Lewis Booker, Ted Boyce, Steve Boydston, Leslie Wilk Braksick, Kathy Brehoney, Bill Brasted, Chris Buermeyer, Stu Burkhammer, John Cairns, Anthony "Corky" Carter, John Casali, Candice Chevailler, Sam Cho, Doug Christoff, Ed Christophersen, Tom Civic, Steve Clarke, George Clum, John Cooper, John Cope, Stephen Covey, Helen Crawford, Karen Cronin, Aubrey Daniels, W. Edwards Deming, Jason DePasquale, Kyle Dotson, John Drebinger, Bill Dwyer, John Elder, Len Evans, Peter Everett, Chris Faron, Steve Fawcett, Jack Finney, Jason Fortney, Amy Gershenoff, Harry Glaser, Sigrid Glenn, Trudy Goldman, Randi Gonzalez, Walt Gould, Dale Gray, Don Groover, Sam Gualardo, Nick Gutermuth, Heidi Hahn, Paul Hamlin, Dwight Harshberger, Kevin Harrington, Charlie Hart, Linda Hayes, Michael Heath, Mark Herweg, Ritchie Hofmann, Bill Hopkins, Carla Housh, Warren Hubler, Marshall Huckaby, Don Hughes, Bowen Huntsman, Brian Iwata, Bill Joiner, Dan Johnson, Dick Johnson, Tim Johnson, Marshall Jones, Russell Jones, Michael Kalsher, Judith Kamin, John Kamp, Gary Karnes, Jerry Kehoe, Keith Keller, John Kello, Jon Juette, Skipper Kendrick, Dan Kett, Nathan Kirk, Hank Knoop, Judy Komaki, Tom Krause, Marianne Krawiec, Bryan Krueger, Harold Kursted, Richard Lack, Juan Landron, Leif Larsen, Ken Lawrence, Jerry Laws, Galen Lehman, Ogden Lindsley, Tim Ludwig, William "Duke" Luksis, Janet Lund, McIlvaine "Mac" Parsons, Bob Madsen, Dick Malott, Mark Mathews, Grainne Matthews, Tom Mawhinney, Joni Mayer, Jerry McDowell, Terry McSween, Carl Metzgar, Jack Michael, Paul Michael, Bob Moran, Charlie Morecraft, Rick Moreno, Maggie Murphy, Larry Needleman, Kim Nutt, Michael O'Toole, Sharon Patterson, Dan Petersen, Sam Phillips, Bill Piercy, Eric Pike, Carol Pilgrim, Gordon Pitz, Frank Polificio, Brian Porter, Jerry Pounds, Ron Preston, Al Prestrude, Jerry Ray, Bill Redmon, John Remmers, Geralyn Richards, Michael Roberts, Scott Rogers, Carol Rowan, Michael Rowe, Nason Russ, Dave Sarkus, Tom Schill, B.F. Skinner, David Sleet, Paul Slovic, Julie Smith, Laura Solomon, Jim Spigener, Ron Starcher, Tom Stewart, Fritz Streff, Scott Stricoff, Beth Sulzer-Azaroff, Don Thompson, Bruce Thyer, Mary Ann Timmerman, Michael Topf, Ron Van Houten, Bob Veazie, Cal von Buseck, Stephen Wachnowsky, Bill Warvel, Dewey Whitmire, Gerald Wilde, George Williamson, Mark Wilson, Richard Winett, Christian Witsch, Susan Wrchota, and Dick Ziebell—thank you all for helping me write this practical book on *The Participation Factor* for occupational safety.

"It ain't so much the things we don't know that get us into trouble; it's the things we know that just ain't so."

—Artemus Ward

Introduction and Orientation

This chapter sets the tone for the entire book—how to get more people participating voluntarily in occupational safety. The key word is "voluntarily." Enforcement works for the short term, but this traditional approach to safety inhibits The Participation Factor. *It influences a dependency mindset—"Just follow the rules and everything will be fine." Independence is better, but interdependency is the optimal paradigm. In an interdependent culture people actively care willingly for the safety of others on a regular basis. This book shows you how to achieve the kind of interdependent work culture needed to attain and sustain an injury-free workplace.*

The key to preventing more work-related injuries is to get more people involved in programs and processes designed to improve occupational health and safety. This is not profound; it's obvious. Yet in so many situations, safety is managed in such a way that involvement is actually inhibited rather than enhanced. For example, common safety slogans, safety incentive programs, and safety metrics actually stifle interpersonal trust and the kinds of proactive conversations and learning needed to prevent injury. In fact, the language we use to talk about safety, with terms like "accident investigation," "loss control," and "root cause," hinders *The Participation Factor*.

It doesn't take major change to turn current situations around and get more employee involvement in occupational health and safety. But it does take a paradigm shift. We need to perceive the problem of workplace injuries differently and intervene differently with regard to the human aspects of safety. Two of the three traditional "E" words for industrial safety are still appropriate and critically important—Engineering and Education. However, to get more participation, we need to replace the third E-word—Enforcement—with another: Empowerment.

This book offers a number of basic strategies for cultivating a work force that feels empowered with regard to safety improvement and regularly does something about it. In other words, this book suggests ways to get more people actively caring for the health and safety of themselves and others. The principles and techniques presented are not based on common sense but on research-tested theory and practical applications. Let's start by reviewing the three E-words that define the traditional approach to safety management.

The Three E-Words of Occupational Safety

For decades occupational safety has focused on the three E-words—Engineering, Education, and Enforcement. This approach has dramatically decreased the number of workplace injuries. Through engineering, the occupational environment has been made safer, and personal protective equipment (PPE) has been continuously improved. Employees are periodically educated about environmental hazards to avoid and safe behaviors to perform, including the appropriate PPE to use in various situations. Then, when employees don't follow the safety rules or instructions taught and reviewed in their safety training classes, enforcement is used in an attempt to motivate compliance.

Figure 1.1 depicts the three E-words as they relate to the three interactive domains of a work culture that determine injury rate. The achievement of an injury-free workplace requires that 1) engineers design the environment, including equipment, tools and operating procedures, so the chance of an injury is minimized, and 2) trainers educate employees with regard to at-risk behaviors to avoid and safe behaviors to perform, including things they can do proactively to reduce the risk of injury to themselves and others. But education alone is often insufficient to motivate either routine participation in injury-prevention efforts or the consistent performance of relatively inconvenient and uncomfortable safe behavior. So employers turn to enforcement as the most efficient way to produce the behaviors they want.

The Enforcement Approach

Enforcement is clearly the most common approach to motivating behavior in our society. It's the universal government method of large-scale control. Just pass a law and enforce it. This tactic does work. Laws define standards and social norms, and since most people want to do the right thing, laws are generally followed and social order is maintained. But of course, this happens only when there is general agreement that the rules are rational and fair. And, if the enforcement system is ineffective, many people will break the rules when noncompliance leads to reinforcing consequences. Highway speeding is a prime example of people choosing to take a risk because enforcement is improbable and the consequences of breaking the rule are so reinforcing, from the excitement of traveling fast to the anticipation of getting to a desired destination quickly.

The biggest problem with the enforcement approach is that it can stifle participation. Threats of punitive consequences for noncompliance will certainly reduce undesirable behavior in situations where the punitive consequence is severe and the probability of getting caught is high, but don't expect people to internalize the rule and follow it when they don't have to. As I explain in Chapter 4, the more external control people experience, the less internal control (self-control) they develop.

Figure 1.1 The three traditional E-words for safety address three domains.

Top-down command-and-control works to a point. But to get beyond the injury-rate plateaus many organizations have reached, more safety-related participation is needed in unsupervised situations. This requires self-persuasion and self-directed behavior, as I cover in Chapter 4. Here I simply want to make the point that the enforcement approach is not sufficient to motivate long-term participation in safety improvement efforts.

Consider, for example, that more than a decade of enforcing the simple and rational life-saving behavior of buckling a vehicle safety belt has led to a nationwide maximum of about 70 percent belt use in the United States. Much higher goals have been set by government officials and optimistic presidents, but don't expect improvement unless some of the strategies covered in this book are applied.

More than twenty-five years ago, I learned the hard way that the enforcement approach can cause more harm than good. Over the years, I've conveyed this lesson to numerous audiences worldwide. I call it the "Blue Book Story." Years ago Johnny Carson told part of it on the *Tonight Show* and portions of my story have been recounted on the Internet. Allow me to tell you the whole "Blue Book Story" and the critical lesson I learned from the experience.

The Blue Book Story

The anecdote gets its title from a common technique, also called a "discussion exam," used in colleges and universities to test students' knowledge of course material. Professors distribute open-ended questions to the class along with blue-covered booklets filled with blank, lined pages. Students write their answers in these so-called "blue books."

Years ago, I stopped using discussion exams in my large classes because it was so time-consuming to read as many as three hundred blue books. Today I use the more efficient but less effective multiple-choice test. But back in 1974, when I began teaching the large sections of Introductory Psychology at Virginia Tech, I used discussion questions and blue books.

One particular exam day was memorable. It was the third exam of the course, and my assistants and I distributed it promptly to each student at 10:00 A.M.—the start of the class. At 10:50 A.M., the end of the fifty-minute class, I clapped my hands and announced loudly, "The exam is over. Please bring your blue books to the front of the room." Three hundred students walked briskly to the front of the classroom, dropped their blue books at the front of the stage, and exited the room.

There was one exception. One student, sitting in the back of the auditorium, ignored my instructions and continued to write in his blue book. I didn't say anything to this "cheater," but proceeded to stack the blue books on the stage. I patiently waited for this student to bring me his blue book, and

Was the calculated risk cheating?

this happened at 11:00 A.M., ten minutes after the class was scheduled to end. By this time, all of the other students had left the room.

The student actually ran to the front of the classroom, waving his exam paper, and shouting, "Wait, Professor Geller—please don't forget my blue book." I gave him penetrating eye contact and asserted, "Keep it, son. You cheated. If I accept your exam, it won't be fair to the rest of the class. Besides, you know my rule about turning in exams on time. This is not the first exam in this class, it's the third. You've already had two opportunities to become aware of my rules about taking an exam in this class."

"Please," the student pleaded, "what if I cross out everything I wrote in the last ten minutes. Wouldn't that make it fair?"

"Sure," I replied. "It would make it fair if you would really eliminate everything you wrote after I announced the end of the exam. But I don't trust you. You tried to beat the system once; you'll try to beat it again. I just cannot accept your blue book."

With that, the student turned and began walking slowly out of the classroom with his head hanging low. He was visibly disheartened. But suddenly, after walking about twenty feet, this student turned 180 degrees and pranced back to the front of the auditorium with an air of confidence I couldn't believe. Then he surprised me by boldly asking, "Sir, do you know who I am?"

Did the student deserve a break?

His question caught me completely off guard. I had to say, "No." And I added, "This is a large classroom, son. You can't expect me to learn the students' names." My comment elicited a big smile on the student's face, and he said, "Good." Then, with lightning speed, he inserted his blue book in the stack of other blue books and sprinted out of the classroom.

The Blue Book Lesson

That's the "Blue Book Story" as reported many years ago on the *Tonight Show* and paraphrased on the Internet. But it's not the whole story. I know, because I was there. That student was obviously creative, but he wasn't fast enough to insert his blue book in the stack without my eyes tracking its location. I gleefully grabbed the student's blue book as he left the room thinking he put one over on his professor. I now knew his name, but he didn't know that I knew.

Put yourself in my shoes. What would you do in that same situation today? Would you flunk the student for cheating, or reward him for his creativity? Would you let him think he got the last laugh, or let him know who is really in

control? Can you relate this incident to workplace safety? Suppose you catch an employee taking a "calculated risk" and now must choose a corrective action plan? Would you follow the enforcement approach and levy a penalty?

In the university setting, cheating ranks among the most heinous behaviors. It's analogous to disregarding a cardinal safety rule in an organizational setting—like failing to lock out a power source on production equipment before adjusting the settings. Given an enforcement mindset, I had no choice. The student had to flunk the exam. Similarly, an employee's failure to follow a primary safety rule is formally recorded, and in some organizations the penalty is a day off without pay.

As I walked back to my office that spring day, however, my blissful thoughts of getting even with this student changed dramatically. I began to question my judgment. Was he really cheating? What were his intentions? Is it possible he didn't hear me signal the end of the exam? He could have been so engrossed in producing results that he didn't hear me or even notice the rest of the class turning in their blue books. In that case, his improper behavior was unintentional human error, and under such circumstances, punishment is inappropriate.

What if the student's risk-taking was actually intentional? In fact, it's likely he heard me call for the exam papers and deliberately ignored me and kept writing. In organizational settings, that's considered a calculated risk or willful disregard of a mandate. The occurrence of such behavior in industry is usually followed by a punitive consequence—no questions asked.

I had problems, however, dealing with so many uncertainties in the classroom situation. Even if the undesirable behavior was purposeful—tantamount to a calculated risk—the nature of the student's intentions or calculations seemed important. What if he was only trying to give me more production? It's possible he didn't even consider his behavior "cheating," but simply an attempt to show his teacher (the supervisor of his work area) how much he knows and how dedicated he is to the task at hand. He may have surmised that I wouldn't mind him taking the extra time. After all, I would be in the room for at least ten minutes collecting the other students' papers and would not be inconvenienced by his extra effort. Perhaps he actually thought I would be pleased with his desire to go beyond the call of duty to achieve more!

It also occurred to me that my expectations may not have been perceived correctly by this student. Did he understand my definition of "cheating"? Sure, I told the class at the start of the first exam that all blue books must be handed in after fifty minutes. However, I didn't say explicitly that anyone not doing this would flunk the exam; I considered that expectation implicitly obvious. But just because it's obvious to me, should it be obvious to every student? And what if the student in question was unaware of my "cardinal rule," either because he was absent or inattentive when I explained the policy? Perhaps he figured production is more important than timeliness, especially when the manager is not inconvenienced.

The Bottom Line

I painfully realized I had no idea whether the student's behavior was human error or a calculated risk. Also, if his undesirable behavior was willful, I didn't have a clue about the possible contributing factors. Why? Because the conversation after the incident was completely one-sided. I had my own bias about what I saw, and that tainted the entire interaction. I learned nothing about the student's perspective, and thus could not make any adjustments to reduce the probability of similar "cheating" behavior occurring again. In this regard, I cheated myself by not having the kind of open and honest interpersonal conversation that could provide insight for continuous improvement.

How often does this happen in the work setting? Do well-intentioned but biased reactions to safety-related incidents stifle learning? Are conversations about property-damage incidents and injuries perceived as more fault-finding than fact-finding? Do employees resist owning up to their contributions to property damage or an injury by making excuses or projecting blame on others? A "yes" answer to any of these questions implies a need for change in your organizational culture. This book offers practical research-based strategies for making such a change.

In fact, it's my sincere opinion that participation in open and frank conversations about how to improve the safety of a work area is key to achieving an injury-free workplace. Of course, conversations need to result in action plans, from equipment redesign and removal of environmental hazards to making adjustments in ongoing work practices. But beneficial change starts with conversations about the need for change. This book tells you how to make that happen. It provides meaningful and realistic things you can do today to help create the kind of culture that facilitates rather than inhibits interpersonal communication about the factors contributing to at-risk behaviors, environmental hazards, near hits, property-damage incidents and personal injuries. I hope I've convinced you that these kinds of interpersonal conversations, critical to learning how to reduce workplace injuries, can be severely hindered in a culture that relies on enforcement to initiate and sustain safe behavior.

Incidentally, the student with the late blue book earned a B+ on that third exam, and he scored an A on the next exam—which he handed in right on time. In fact, he got an A in my class and majored in psychology. To this day he doesn't know I know his name, unless he has heard one of the many reports of this incident, including the numerous times I've told the story—to large convention audiences and every introductory psychology class I've taught since the one he took in 1974.

I often reflect on what might have happened if I had given that student a failing grade. Would he have felt "cheated" and perhaps have performed much worse in my class? Could a top-down enforcement approach to the "cheating" situation have turned the student off to psychology and influenced him to choose another major? Could one unfortunate incident have had so much influence on this individual's future? I hope you see that "yes" is a possible answer to each of these questions.

Now, I ask you: Do you know anyone who is less involved in certain safety-related activities at work because of an incident related to enforcement? People have long memories of punitive consequences, especially when they believe their position was not understood or they were treated unfairly. Such negative interactions can instill a mindset that may inhibit participation in subsequent activities, even those only remotely related to the original incident.

Positive Discipline

Because negative consequences can severely inhibit learning and constructive interaction, the all too common penalty of sending an employee home without pay should be avoided (Grote 1995). The negative feelings or attitudes associated with docking a person's pay will only interfere with the lesson you want the person to learn from such punishment. In addition, the employee will undoubtedly remember this punitive and "unfair" (from his or her perspective) experience for years and use this negative baggage as an excuse to shun voluntary participation in safety programs.

You can avoid this problem by simply changing the focus of the temporary dismissal policy from "punishment" to "learning and corrective action." It's not about enforcement and retribution; it's about finding a meaningful way to reduce the future occurrence of the undesirable behavior. Send the employee home with pay. The employee does not get a paid vacation day for the safety infraction. Rather, the individual must evaluate the calculated risk carefully and decide what can be done to reduce the possibility of a recurrence. Because the employee's wages are not withheld, this appraisal is not tainted by a negative or hostile attitude.

One option for the employee is to not return to work. More specifically, it should be emphasized that individuals should consider whether their personal priorities are consistent with safety being a company core "value." In other words, employees must choose to improve or choose to work someplace else. This is not punishment (or "discipline," as mislabeled by industry), but an opportunity to consider whether the work culture is a good match for the employees' interests, talents, and values. Such "positive discipline" is a valuable learning experience en route to continuous improvement.

If an individual chooses to remain employed, he or she must develop a personal corrective action plan for avoiding the undesirable behavior in question and performing alternative safe behavior. Elsewhere I detail a precise behavioral analysis to guide the development of a practical plan for corrective action (Geller 2000a, 2001d). Here I only want to make the point that changing the focus of a "dismissal policy" from enforcement and punishment to learning and corrective action can eliminate the negative impact of such incidents on future participation.

It's critical, of course, for a supervisor or safety leader to review an employee's plan for corrective action as soon as he or she returns to work. Both parties need to agree that the plan is reasonable, feasible, and cost-effective. It's likely that joint understanding and appreciation of a suitable action plan will require significant discussion, consensus building, and refinement of the corrective action document. I discuss ways to meet this challenge in Chapter 6. The final version of the proposal should be signed by both parties to signify mutual agreement for the program procedures and interpersonal commitment to support efforts to make the action plan truly remedial.

Working to Avoid Failure

Besides stifling communication about injuries and how to prevent them, enforcement is a failure-oriented approach. In other words, it puts people in the unpleasant motivational state of "working to avoid failure." They follow the safety rules to avoid negative consequences. Such a mindset can bias a person's entire view of safety. They might consider safety a "necessary evil," and avoid thinking about it as much as possible.

People prefer working to achieve success rather than to avoid failure. Think about it. In which situations do you feel better about accomplishing a certain task—when you can visualize the gain of positive consequences following the assignment or when your thoughts focus on negative outcomes expected if the job is not completed? In both cases, motivation to work on the task comes from the anticipation of consequences. But attitude toward the assignment will be more positive if the focus is on achieving success rather than avoiding failure. Even though anticipated results are motivating behavior in both situations, people feel more "free" when the controlling consequences are positive than when they are negative (Skinner 1971).

I see this differential perspective in my students, and this affects their attitudes toward my class. Students with an achievement-oriented perspective see my course as an opportunity to earn a high grade, to improve their grade point average, and sometimes even to learn. In contrast, students working to avoid failure view attending my class as a requirement, something they "got" to do rather than "get" to do. They look for ways to beat the system, like skipping class and copying the notes from a classmate.

Notice that the same consequences are available for all students. Any student can receive a positive grade for success or a negative grade for failure. What determines the differential perspectives? Actually, a multitude of factors influence a student's orientation toward success versus failure, from prior personal experiences and expectations to individual motives, perceptions, and daily consequences in the class itself.

Similarly, whether employees view their participation in safety as an opportunity or a requirement is influenced by numerous factors, including the results of past participation in safety efforts. My primary point here is that an enforcement paradigm is detrimental to the kind of success-oriented attitude needed to motivate employees to do more than follow the rules. If we want people to view safety as more than a requirement and to go beyond the call of duty to achieve an injury-free workplace, we need to eliminate factors that put people in a failure-oriented mode.

Take a look at the runner illustrated on the next page. This athlete will surely start running as fast as he can. But how long will he run? Will he keep running when the coach is not around to threaten negative consequences for failure? Will he practice on his own to increase his speed? Will he hold himself accountable to be the best he can be? A "yes" answer to any of these questions is likely if the runner can put himself in the mental framework of "working to succeed" instead of "working to avoid failure." However, the enforcement context established by the coach makes the

Working to avoid failure limits self-accountability.

failure-oriented approach more probable and makes a "no" answer to the questions more likely.

Employees often have an achievement mindset when it comes to quality and productivity, and thus they work for production goals without direct supervision. The enforcement approach may be used to increase the production of an organization, but it is not used exclusively. Employees' salaries are logically linked to whatever a company delivers for profit, and productivity and quality goals are usually stated in terms of achievement. Outcomes related to profit are recorded and tracked as individual or team accomplishments and are periodically accompanied by rewards or recognition.

In contrast, safety is most often discussed with regard to avoiding failure or controlling losses. Keeping score for safety means tracking and recording losses or injuries. Companies are ranked with regard to number of "OSHA recordables," "lost-time injuries," or their "total recordable injury rate (TRIR)." Not only are such statistics reactive and unreliable (cf. O'Brien 2000), they promote a negative motivational scheme that is likely to take a back seat to the positive system used for productivity and quality.

An enforcement approach to safety holds people accountable to comply with particular rules or mandates, but it decreases self-accountability—the personal responsibility needed to do things for safety when working alone. This book offers various ways to give safety an achievement focus, thereby providing a system that motivates more participation, even when employees work alone with no one around to hold them accountable.

From a Dependent to an Interdependent Work Culture

Relying on enforcement to motivate safety can also cultivate a dependency out-look toward injury prevention. That is, work cultures with a command-and-control paradigm—that safety is a "condition of employment"—can give the impression that injury prevention means only "complying with the safety rules," no more and no less. In this kind of workplace, employees become dependent on the organization to keep them injury-free with machinery safe-guards, personal protective equipment, and rules to follow. Workers in a dependent culture do not talk about safety very much. A near hit, property-damage incident, or minor injury is rarely recorded. Why should workers report a mishap that implies carelessness or failure to follow some safety rule? Why should employees bring up something that could lead to embarrassment or even a punitive consequence for not following the rules?

In dependent cultures, safety gets significant attention and participation only when a serious injury occurs that cannot be hidden, and then people scurry about looking for a quick-fix solution. Often the TRIR of these organi-zations is quite low, but for the wrong reasons. Many recordable injuries are just not reported. Employees refer to this malady as the "bloody pocket syndrome."

Many organizational cultures have progressed from dependence to inde-pendence with regard to occupational safety. Both management and line workers realize that the three traditional "E's" of safety—engineering, edu-cation, and enforcement—are not sufficient to maintain an injury-free workplace. It's understood that people need to take personal responsibility for safety in their organization. Workers need to be on continual lookout for envi-ronmental hazards and adjust their behavior accordingly.

This independent state seems natural for many adults in the United States. From childhood the majority of U.S. residents have been taught an individu-alistic, win/lose perspective, sustained by such popular slogans as "Nice guys finish last," "The squeaky wheel gets the grease," "You have to blow your own horn," and "No one can fill your shoes like you." Furthermore, grades in school, the legal system, most sporting events, and even interpersonal con-versation promote a win/lose attitude.

Safety participation is higher in the independent culture than in the dependent culture, but it's not optimal. An interdependent culture facilitates

The U.S. culture promotes a win/lose perspective.

the most involvement in safety improvement efforts, but such a culture does not come easily, especially when so many of life's trials and tribulations seem to reflect individualism over collectivism (Triandis 1977, 1985). Just the commute to work, for example, puts some people in a competitive win/lose state, adding to the challenge of developing an interdependent work culture.

A mature safety culture is interdependent. In these organizations people feel empowered every day to actively care for the safety and health of others. They go beyond the call of duty to participate in safety-related efforts, including the reporting and analysis of all injuries and property-damage incidents. They look for ways to make environmental conditions and behavior safer; and when they find one, they intervene with appropriate consideration of relevant person factors, as detailed in this book. Even though employees in an interdependent work culture do not think an injury will happen to them,

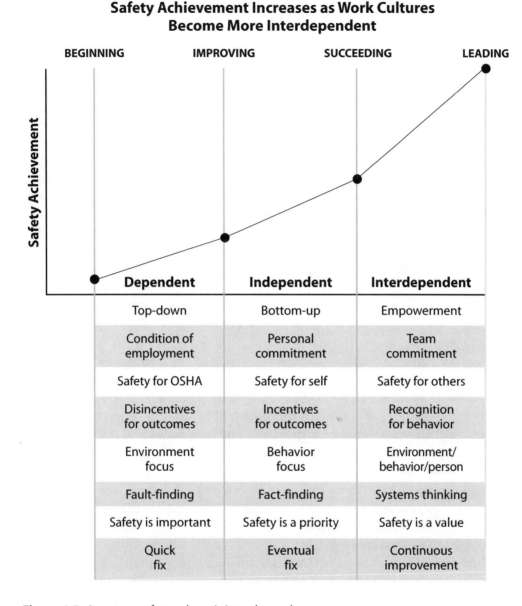

Safety Achievement Increases as Work Cultures Become More Interdependent

Dependent	Independent	Interdependent
Top-down	Bottom-up	Empowerment
Condition of employment	Personal commitment	Team commitment
Safety for OSHA	Safety for self	Safety for others
Disincentives for outcomes	Incentives for outcomes	Recognition for behavior
Environment focus	Behavior focus	Environment/ behavior/person
Fault-finding	Fact-finding	Systems thinking
Safety is important	Safety is a priority	Safety is a value
Quick fix	Eventual fix	Continuous improvement

Figure 1.2 A mature safety culture is interdependent.

they remain motivated to participate in safety-improvement efforts because they realize an incident will happen to someone unless everyone actively cares for the achievement of a Total Safety Culture.

Figure 1.2 summarizes this section on dependent, independent, and inter-dependent safety cultures. By examining the words and slogans associated with each type of culture, you can estimate whether your safety culture is beginning, improving, succeeding, or leading. More importantly, the figure defines the ultimate vision for occupational safety and health. To achieve the ideal Total Safety Culture in which all employees actively care for the safety and health of each other, behaviors and attitudes consistent with the qualities of an interdependent culture need to be cultivated. This book shows you how to make this happen. An injury-free workplace requires continual attention to *The Participation Factor,* meaning specific things must be accomplished daily to encourage more involvement in safety-improvement efforts.

Some methods of increasing participation are relatively simple, like changing the language we use to communicate about safety and developing an achievement-oriented scoring system to track safety progress. Other strategies for increasing participation involve the implementation of a certain kind of safety process, such as interdependent coaching procedures during which employees observe the work practices of their coworkers and then involve the coworkers in constructive conversation to identify environmental hazards and barriers to safe work practices.

The guidelines and practical techniques presented in this book are not new or earthshaking. Numerous organizations I have visited are already applying many of the action plans described here and as a result have dramatically increased employee involvement. "It's not rocket science," I've heard many safety professionals say when referring to the principles and procedures described in this book. But when hearing this popular assertion about psychological factors, I must add (usually only to myself), "My recommendations for improving the human dynamics of safety are based on scientific research, and they are terribly important. The psychology of a situation can make that situation successful or unsuccessful, pleasant or unpleasant, meaningful or meaningless—and safe or unsafe."

Furthermore, while the techniques described in this book are straightforward and inexpensive to put in place, they can be difficult to initiate and sustain. After all, we are talking about change, and change is never easy, especially when the ultimate target is an entire work culture. But anything you do to fuel *The Participation Factor* for occupational safety can make a difference. So decide on a few specific action plans you can work on today that are consistent with your vision of an injury-free workplace.

In Conclusion

In this initial chapter, I have defined the basic purpose of this book—to teach principles and practical procedures for increasing employee involvement in safety-related activities. The focus is on the human dynamics of a work culture, and what can be done to get more people actively caring on a regular basis for the safety and health of themselves and others. This boils down to developing a greater sense of personal responsibility for occupational safety throughout an organization. In other words, this book shows you how to successively approximate the kind of interdependent work culture in which the employees do not need others to hold them accountable for safety participation, but instead hold themselves accountable to do whatever it takes to attain and sustain an injury-free workplace.

My recommendations are not based on intuition or common sense, but on reliable scientific research and successful industrial applications. Some suggestions will contradict traditional approaches to the management of occupational safety, such as the theme of this chapter—the de-emphasis of the enforcement approach. I hope the disadvantages of this E-word with regard to motivating more participation are now obvious. To get more involvement in safety improvement we need to focus on another E-word— empowerment.

By empowerment, I don't mean giving people authority to do more. Many employees are tired of hearing this word because it's often viewed as a management strategy for getting them to do more with less. "You're going to empower me? Great! Just what I need! As if I don't already have enough to do." This kind of "empowerment" does not increase personal responsibility and participation for occupational safety. The next chapter explains the kind of empowerment that does increase involvement in safety-improvement activities. I'm not talking about *getting* empowered, but rather *feeling* empowered. There's a big difference, as you'll see when reading the next chapter.

"The greatest reward for doing is the opportunity to do more."
—Jonas Salk

The Power of Empowerment

Without true empowerment, an injury-free workplace cannot be achieved and maintained. This chapter explains why by describing five belief states that determine whether a person feels empowered—self-efficacy, response-efficacy, outcome-expectancy, personal control, and optimism. Understanding these ingredients of empowerment enables the design and delivery of safety messages and training classes that facilitate participation. When people feel empowered, they are ready and willing to get involved. Thus, empowerment—as defined here—is essential for The Participation Factor. *A work force empowered for occupational safety actively cares every day to eliminate hazards and prevent personal injury.*

In the management literature, empowerment typically refers to delegating authority or responsibility, or sharing decision making (Conger and Kanungo 1988). However, a different perspective of empowerment can be found in the psychological literature (Geller 2001d). Here empowerment is a matter of personal perception. Do you feel empowered and more responsible? Can you handle the additional assignment? Do you want to learn more and develop more skills so you can better deal with your additional responsibility?

The worker illustrated on the next page is clearly overloaded. As a result, she can't remember whom she called or why she even made the phone call. How unusual is this? Has this ever happened to you? In the midst of doing several things at once you dial a phone number, but by the time the phone is answered you're into another task or at least thinking of another assignment. The result: you forget who you were calling and why. This is not empowerment. You might be in charge of many job tasks, but do you feel in control? Someone might have "empowered" you to do more, but do you *feel* more empowered?

Being empowered is not the same as feeling empowered.

This psychological view of empowerment is directly relevant to increasing participation in safety-improvement activities. When people feel empowered they want to get more involved. They believe they can make a difference and they feel good about the extra responsibility. Yes, I'm talking about feeling states—the kind of psychology referred to as "warm fuzzies" or "soft science" in industry. We can do things to change people's feeling states. By altering environmental conditions and behavioral contingencies in certain ways, we can increase people's sense of empowerment and thereby their level of participation. To do this, we need to understand where real empowerment comes from. The quick answer is that empowerment is determined by our personal beliefs. What kinds of beliefs? Now that requires a longer answer.

You Must Believe

"Believe in yourself, and you can achieve anything." "Self-affirmations are the key to success." "Prosperity begins with self-confidence."

I'm sure you've heard statements like these before. Each reflects a common theme among motivational speakers. The focus is to convince audiences to believe in themselves. The orators present a powerful rationale for self-confidence, often by presenting their own hardship stories and courageous triumphs at overcoming impossible odds. Sometimes they tell us of the trials and tribulations of national heroes who surmounted countless obstacles in rising to enviable heights. In all of these cases, the key contributor to eventual success is the belief that triumph will happen.

There is empirical and theoretical support for the assertion that believing you can do something is the first step toward doing it. The academic term for this belief is self-efficacy, and it has been the topic of many research articles and theoretical proposals. Most notable is Albert Bandura's 1997 book, titled simply *Self-Efficacy*. Here, in 604 pages of fine print, the author makes a strong case for self-efficacy being the most central and critical concept in applied psychology. Let's consider the main features of this concept.

Self-Efficacy: Can I Do It?

Self-efficacy reflects a "can do" attitude. It refers to a person's perception that he or she can organize the relevant resources and execute the procedures necessary to reach a certain goal. Numerous studies have shown that people who score relatively high on a measure of self-efficacy gain more from psychotherapy and perform better at a wide range of tasks. They show greater ability and motivation to solve complex problems at work, and they have better health and safety habits (Bandura 1982; Betz and Hackett 1986; Hackett et al. 1992).

Self-Efficacy versus Self-Esteem. Self-efficacy is not the same as self-esteem, but self-efficacy contributes to self-esteem, and vice versa. Self-esteem reflects a general sense of self-worth, as in "I am valuable," whereas self-efficacy refers to feeling successful or competent at a particular task. While self-esteem remains rather constant across situations, self-efficacy is task-focused and therefore can vary markedly from one circumstance to another.

Building Self-Efficacy. When you ask someone, "Do you have what you need?" you are checking for feelings of self-efficacy. Unfortunately, it's not easy to get an honest answer to this question, because people often hesitate to admit they are incompetent at something. Really, who likes to say, "I can't do it"? Instead, we try to maintain the appearance of self-efficacy.

Losing a sense of self-efficacy can be devastating, however. The perception of low self-efficacy saps one's motivation and can lead to feelings of helplessness. I see this in my students all too often, and it's usually the result of their not keeping up with the readings or class assignments. They miss a few classes or fail to complete their homework assignments. Then, because lessons build on principles and concepts learned from previous information presented in class or in the reading assignment, my subsequent lectures and exercises become more difficult to understand. As a result, some students simply give up, resigned to doing only enough to avoid failing.

In a one-to-one teaching or coaching relationship it's possible to observe an individual's behavior and determine whether the person is ready for the next lesson. In other words, it's important to know how competent an individual is at a particular task before asking for more. If we understand the student's baseline competence, we can avoid the possibility of lowering self-efficacy and motivation by making the next learning step too large. The coach in the following illustration understands this principle. He builds the student's confidence in feeling competent to do the task by allowing the student to experience instant success. Then he makes the task increasingly more difficult (within the student's capabilities), in this case by having him stand farther from the target on successive trials.

The key is to reduce the chance the learner will make an error and feel lowered self-efficacy or self-confidence. When you reward small-win achievements with social approval, you build self-efficacy and enable support from the self-fulfilling prophecy. After feeling competent at a task, people expect more success and work harder to make success happen again.

Small steps to success build self-efficacy.

Self-Efficacy and Training. The aim of good training is to give participants certain skills or competencies. For example, effective training in safety coaching (Geller 1995) involves teaching specific procedural steps for 1) observing and analyzing another person's behaviors, 2) delivering supportive and corrective feedback, 3) developing an improvement plan, and 4) obtaining commitment for change and follow-up. But effective safety coaches need more than these skills. They need self-efficacy.

Participants in a training program show what they know on written exams and demonstrate their behavioral expertise through role-play. Skillful trainers improve skills through behavior-based feedback. In other words, through practice and feedback, participants develop competence and a belief that they can accomplish the task at hand.

Mastery at something usually builds self-efficacy, and vice versa. But having one does not mean having the other. People may have the skills to excel at a certain task but lack the confidence to execute the required behaviors. On the other hand, people can have more self-efficacy than warranted by their ability to perform. That's what we mean when we label a person "over-confident." But, even when people have both self-efficacy and adequate skills to perform a certain safety process, they won't participate over the long term unless they also have response-efficacy.

Response-Efficacy: Will the Technique Work?

Response-efficacy refers to one's belief that a certain technique or strategy will actually produce a desired outcome. Thus, it's not enough to know what to do and have the confidence to do it. The participant must believe it's worth doing. People can have the skills and self-efficacy to perform safety coaching, for example, but they will not coach on a regular basis unless they believe the coaching process will actually improve safety.

Response-Efficacy and Training. The concept of response-efficacy has critical implications for safety training. Specifically, it's not enough to teach participants the procedural steps for conducting a certain safety process. Trainees also need to be convinced the technique has the potential to prevent personal injury. How can we accomplish this?

Response-efficacy is most commonly taught by presenting statistics. Research data are presented that show significant improvement as a result of a particular intervention strategy. This approach is effective for research presentations, but it might not convince the average employee.

Case Studies over Statistics. I don't mean to imply that employees can't understand statistics. My point is, they won't necessarily relate to them. It's better to get more personal and relevant when trying to "sell" the value of an intervention process to a work force. Research on risk perception, for example, has shown that people become more concerned or outraged about an issue when individual case studies are used rather than group statistics (Sandman 1991; Slovic 1991). (That's the reason politicians point to specific individuals in their audiences when attempting to gain support for a particular issue or plan of action.)

Personal testimonies provide a powerful image. Listeners can relate to an individual's story and put themselves in the same situation. Two kinds of testimony can increase response-efficacy: 1) a personal account of an injury that could have been prevented by the safety technique, and 2) an anecdote about someone who avoided injury by using the technique.

Outcome-Expectancy: Is the Outcome Worth the Effort?

"Outcome-expectancy" is the consequence one expects to receive when practicing a safety technique. One of the most important legacies of B. F. Skinner (1953, 1974) is "selection by consequences," which means behavior is motivated by events or conditions that follow it. In other words, we motivate ourselves to do or not do something by anticipating what positive consequences we expect to gain from our participation and/or what negative consequences we expect to avoid. Even the couch potato in the illustration at the right is motivated by a consequence, although the server may be asking for too large a step, given the observed level of self-efficacy.

So, we might believe we can do something (self-efficacy) and believe what we do will have a certain effect (response-efficacy), but we won't perform unless we also believe the effect is worth working for (outcome-expectancy). Will our labor reap sufficient benefits to outweigh the costs, including our effort? In safety, for example, a group might believe their safety record is good enough, given that they see very few coworkers getting seriously injured. The potential gain from an inconvenient safety process might seem too small to justify the amount of extra effort required for implementation.

Here again it's more useful to "sell" with a case study than a statistic like "total recordable injury rate." It's also important to point out the difference between an individualistic mindset and a collectivistic perspective, as introduced in Chapter 1. From an individual outlook, the probability of an injury is miniscule. As a result, the outcome from participation in a safety effort can seem insignificant. In contrast, interdependent thinkers take a wider view. They recognize that *someone* will benefit from large-scale participation in a safety process.

You could show, for example, the details of a single injury that occurred in your plant and explain how an intervention like the one being taught could

Consequences can motivate the achievement of "stretch" goals.

have prevented it. In this way, you are inspiring both response-efficacy and outcome-expectancy—the belief that the intervention process can work and produce an outcome everyone should want and be willing to work for.

In Summary

Figure 2.1 summarizes the three beliefs that contribute to feeling empowered. Motivation to perform a task comes from outcome-expectancy—the belief that completing the task will gain a positive consequence or avoid a negative one. As Dale Carnegie put it in 1936 in his classic best seller, *How to Win Friends and Influence People,* "Every act you have ever performed since the day you were born was performed because you wanted something" (p. 62). Incidentally, Carnegie did not claim this motivation principle to be common sense, but referred to the research and scholarship of B. F. Skinner.

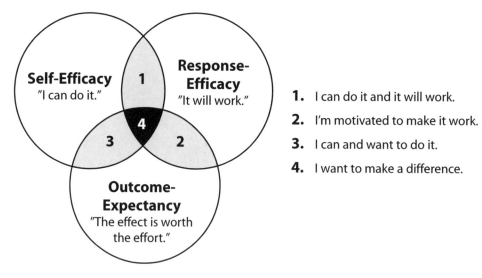

Figure 2.1 Three person states influence empowerment.

1. I can do it and it will work.
2. I'm motivated to make it work.
3. I can and want to do it.
4. I want to make a difference.

Some consequences are soon, certain, and sizable, and thus are powerful motivators. The pedestrian in the illustration below, for example, will most likely comply with the "Don't walk" sign. He sees the possibility of immediate,

Soon, certain and sizable consequences are powerful motivators.

certain, and sizable negative consequences if he walks at the wrong time. With such obvious impending threats, he might in fact follow the advice of the second signal—RUN! Outcome-expectancies motivate him to take certain action.

What about the employee illustrated below? Some behaviors are not supported by soon, certain, and sizable consequences, and can seem like a "waste" of time. In many work cultures the idea of employee-driven safety suggestions has long since passed. The suggestion boxes are empty. Why? Answering this question could involve the three belief states discussed here—self-efficacy, response-efficacy, and outcome-expectancy.

Although it's likely every employee could offer a helpful safety suggestion, a management-driven, technical approach to safety (as in the dependency work culture described in Chapter 1) can lead to the belief that giving advice about preventing injury is beyond the expertise of the average line worker. As such, employees can actually believe they lack the knowledge, skills, resources, or support to submit a useful and meaningful suggestion for improving safety in their workplace.

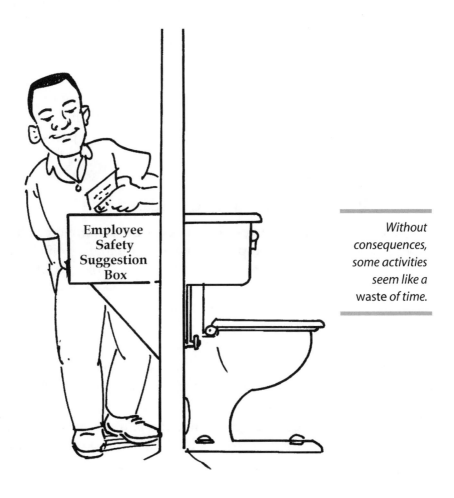

Without consequences, some activities seem like a waste of time.

It is more likely, however, that a lack of response-efficacy rather than a lack of self-efficacy is responsible for low participation in a safety-suggestion system. In other words, employees are more likely to believe their suggestions will not be instrumental in achieving a safety improvement than to believe they lack the ability to offer a practical recommendation. Why? You know the answer—consequences. As more than one employee has told me, "I offered a safety suggestion years ago, and no one listened; the hazard is still there."

When employees receive timely feedback regarding the utility and feasibility of their safety suggestions, they develop a belief that their recommendations are at least considered. Maximum response-efficacy occurs when employees see a change in their workplace as the result of their safety suggestions. Even better would be a system that empowered workers to put their own safety suggestions into effect. Of course, for this to happen the participants would need to have all three of the beliefs discussed here. After successfully implementing their safety suggestions, each of these belief states would be enhanced further. The result: more employee empowerment to continuously improve the safety of their workplace.

I hope you not only understand the difference between self-efficacy, response-efficacy, and outcome-expectancy, but can apply them to a variety of situations that require more employee participation. I have shown the relevance of these beliefs to developing and delivering training and to activating a more participative safety-suggestion system. Now let's consider the role of these beliefs in the design of fear messages to motivate participation in safety-related activities.

Fear Messages: Scared Safe

Imagine you're watching television, and during a commercial break a public service announcement attempts to persuade you to use vehicle safety belts. A teenage girl is shown sitting in a rocking chair looking out a window. She says, "I'm not sick or anything. I could go out more, but since the car crash, I just don't . . . the crash wasn't Dad's fault. I go for walks with my father after dark . . . that way I don't get, you know, stared at."

The girl turns enough to reveal a large, ugly scar on her face, which was previously hidden from view. She continues, "It doesn't hurt anymore." Then an announcer says off-camera, "Car crashes kill two ways: right away and then little by little. Wear your seat belt and live!"

What does your common sense tell you about the impact of this kind of message—one that tries to scare people into being safe? Should we use fear-arousing messages to increase safety-related behaviors? Do fear tactics work?

A Classic Field Study

Some people's common sense tells them that fear appeals are no good: The anxiety or emotional reaction caused by a scary message may interfere with viewer's attention and retention (Lazarus 1980). Or, viewers might deny or repress fear in order to maintain their comfort level. This is probably the common sense of many safety professionals, because of a study showing that using scare tactics failed to get people to buckle up (Geller 1989; Robertson 1976).

The basic approach of the study was to present verbal messages and pictures to warn audiences that any inconvenience or discomfort is minor compared to the disability or disfigurement resulting from a vehicle crash. The opening scenario of this section, for example, was used in the most widely known behavior-based evaluation of public service announcements presented on television. This large-scale study was conducted in the early 1970s by Leon Robertson and colleagues (Robertson et al. 1974).

Six different safety-belt messages, four using a scare tactic like the one above, were shown during the day and during prime time on one cable of a dual-cable TV system. The 6,400 homes on Cable System A received the safety-belt messages 943 times over a nine-month period. This amounted to an average exposure of two to three presentations per person every week. The 7,400 homes on Cable System B were the control group, and received no public service announcements about safety belts.

The impact of the safety messages was evaluated by daily field observations of safety-belt use at fourteen community sites, for one month before and throughout the nine months of the campaign. Vehicle license plate numbers were recorded and later matched with each owner's name and address from the files of the state department of motor vehicles. The TV viewers did not know they were in an experiment, and the field observers could not know the group assignment of the vehicles they observed. This represents one of the most rigorous large-scale behavioral tests of a media safety message.

The results were disappointing. Overall, mean safety-belt use among male and female drivers was 8.4 percent and 11.3 percent, respectively, for the treatment group and 8.2 percent and 10.3 percent, respectively, for the no-treatment control group. These findings were published in 1974 in the *American Journal of Public Health* along with the authors' conclusion that "television campaigns do not have any effect on use of safety belts" (Robertson et al. 1974, p. 1071).

A prime reason for the results given by transportation officials and communication researchers was that four of the six TV spots were based on a scare tactic. It was assumed that the fear emotion interfered with attention or learning, or simply caused denial. This conclusion and interpretation spread throughout the safety community and contributed to a common belief that scare tactics aren't effective for safety campaigns (Leventhal, Shafer, and Panagis 1983; Sutton 1982; Winett 1986).

However, the results of follow-up research on the impact of fear appeals require a change in this "common sense." A comprehensive review of various studies of fear appeals since the 1970s shows quite conclusively that scare tactics work well when they include self-efficacy, response-efficacy, and outcome-expectancy messages (Hale and Dillard 1995; Witte and Allen 2000). Let me explain.

The Successful Scare Tactic

Let's relate these three beliefs to the design of an effective fear appeal. First, a realistic scare tactic tells an audience they need to do something to avoid a negative consequence. That's the motivation component reflected in an outcome-expectancy. To be effective, however, the message must do more than scare. It must demonstrate a straightforward behavioral strategy for avoiding the negative consequence (response-efficacy), and present the safety countermeasure in a way that convinces the audience they can apply it successfully (self-efficacy). Research has shown quite convincingly that this kind of fear appeal will produce the most beneficial behavior change.

Keep in mind, however, the conclusion mentioned earlier of Paul Slovic (1991), Peter Sandman (1991) and colleagues from their rigorous risk perception research. Collective statistics don't scare us nearly as much as individual case studies. That's why it's so important to cultivate the kind of corporate culture in which employees willingly discuss their injuries and near hits with work groups.

However, testimonies must do more than convince people there's a risk in their work space. They must do more than arouse fear or anxiety. To be effective at motivating desirable behavior, they must offer convincing strategies for avoiding the injury and assure audiences they have the time, skills, and tools to apply the injury-prevention procedure. In this way, the scare tactic motivates people to avoid the aroused fear by acting constructively in ways that truly contribute to injury prevention.

Why Didn't the Opening Scare Tactic Work?

I'll bet you see several aspects of the opening scenario that should have made it effective. It displayed an individual case in a way that typically provokes outcome-expectancy. In other words, most viewers can relate to the teenager and the aversive consequences she is experiencing. Furthermore, using a vehicle safety belt is easy, so self-efficacy should be implied as a way to avoid the negative outcome. And surely a viewer could see that safety-belt use would have prevented the girl's face from smashing into the windshield. Thus, response-efficacy was implied.

So where's the problem? Why didn't this and similar scare tactics work in 1974 to increase safety-belt use? One can only speculate, of course, but there are a number of possibilities. It's my guess that the year was a critical factor. In fact, I think a scare tactic like that would work today.

Readers who were driving in 1974 will recall a few key differences between then and now that probably hindered response-efficacy in the 1970s. First, vehicles in those days frequently had only lap belts, which do not prevent heads from slamming into windshields. More importantly, it was once common to hear of individuals whose lives were saved because they were not buckled up. "Uncle Joe was thrown clear of the crash and therefore did not burn in the fire." "Luckily, Aunt Mary was unbuckled and thus able to escape from her sinking vehicle."

Note also that the use of vehicle safety belts was very low in the 1970s. While today it's natural to see people buckled up, in those days safety-belt use was the exception, not the rule. Thus, it's likely the opening scenario would have benefited from showing people buckled up. However, the TV actors in those days buckled up even less frequently than the general public (Geller 1988, 1989). Back then there was a different culture with regard to vehicle safety belts. Bottom line: It's difficult to scare people into performing a certain behavior when it's easy to see that almost everyone else is not practicing the desired response.

In Summary

Perhaps the subtitle of this section reminded some readers of a program designed to reduce juvenile delinquency—"Scared Straight." For this intervention, teenagers who have broken the law spend the day in a prison where they encounter a number of tough, "in-your-face" inmates. These inmates give the juveniles a taste of prison reality in an attempt to "scare them straight."

The results of this program have been mixed. Most teenagers are alarmed and horrified by their prison experience. But, when they return to their neighborhoods and peer groups, many (if not most) continue their destructive and/or illegal behavior patterns. Why? You know the answer.

Those who failed to change didn't receive strategies (response-efficacy) they believed they could actually perform effectively (self-efficacy) in order to avoid the negative consequences they were scared into wanting to avoid. Thus, the "scared straight" tactic usually only influences *one* of the three beliefs needed to affect beneficial behavior change—outcome-expectancy.

Personal Control and Optimism

Understanding and increasing empowerment requires the consideration of two additional psychological states—personal control and optimism. Each relates directly to self-efficacy, and all three of these belief states influence one another. People with high self-efficacy have a high sense of personal control and optimism, and vice versa. And feeling optimistic usually means an individual feels in control of a particular situation, which means having self-efficacy— the knowledge, skills, and resources needed to achieve a goal. These belief states are distinctive, however, and it's important to appreciate their unique characteristics, because doing so can lead to creating ways to enhance one or more of the belief states and thereby facilitate true empowerment.

Personal Control

Personal control is the feeling that "I am in control." J. B. Rotter (1966) used the term *locus of control* in describing the location—internal or external—of forces controlling a person's life. Those with an *internal* locus of control believe they usually have direct personal control over significant life events as a result of their knowledge, skill, and abilities. They believe they are captain of their life's ship.

In contrast, persons with an *external* locus of control believe factors like chance, luck, or fate play important roles in their lives. In a sense, externals believe they are victims, or sometimes beneficiaries, of circumstances beyond their direct personal control (Rotter 1966; Rushton 1984).

Personal control is one of the most researched individual difference dimensions in psychology. Since Dr. Rotter developed the first measure of the relationship between perceptions of personal control and other variables in 1966, more than 2,000 studies have investigated it (Hunt 1993). Internals are more achievement-oriented and health-conscious than externals. They are less prone to distress and more likely to seek medical treatment when they need it (Nowicki and Strickland 1973; Strickland 1989). In addition, having an internal locus of control helps reduce chronic pain, facilitates psychological and physical adjustment to illness and surgery, and hastens recovery from some diseases (Taylor 1991). Internals perform better at jobs that allow them to set their own pace, whereas externals work better when a machine controls the pace (Eskew and Riche 1982; Phares 1991).

Stress vs. Distress. Elsewhere I have emphasized the critical distinction between stress and distress (Geller 2000b, 2001d). Stress is commonly discussed as something bad. When people say they feel "stressed," they usually mean they feel overwhelmed, like the worker illustrated on page 20. But this feeling state is not "stress," it's *dis*tress. The difference between these two states is the perception of control.

The first definition of stress in *The American Heritage Dictionary* (1992) is "importance, significance, or emphasis placed on something" (p. 1205). So when we are stressed, we are focused. We are motivated to make something happen. We feel empowered, especially if we also have self-efficacy, response-efficacy, and outcome-expectancy. The person who asserts, "I work best under pressure" understands the benefits of stress. Hans Selye, the Austrian-born founder of stress research, said, "Complete freedom from stress is death" (Selye 1974, p. 32).

Distress is the bad feeling state. It is defined as "anxiety or suffering . . . severe strain resulting from exhaustion or an accident" (*The American Heritage Dictionary* 1991, p. 410) or "suffering of body or mind; pain, anguish; trouble, misfortune . . . a condition of desperate need" (*The New Merriam-Webster Dictionary* 1989, p. 224). The workers depicted in the illustration below are experiencing distress. When stressors are managed effectively, distress is converted to stress. How can we facilitate such a transformation? You guessed it: Distress turns to stress when perceptions of personal control are increased.

Stressors are managed by gaining personal control.

Influencing Personal Control. Anything that increases self-efficacy or response-efficacy should increase perceptions of personal control. So giving people more knowledge, resources, and support should increase personal control and transform distress into stress. But personal control is a personal perception; it's in the eyes of the beholder. Stephen Covey (1989) recommends we distinguish between our "Circle of Concern" and our "Circle of Influence," and focus our efforts on the Circle of Influence. In other words, excessive concern about factors we can't control, from the weather and politics to various management decisions that can affect our lives, depreciates our sense of personal control and contributes to distress. It's healthy to admit there are things we are concerned about but have little influence over. Then, when negative consequences occur outside of our domain of personal influence, we do not attribute personal blame and reduce our sense of empowerment.

Sometimes events occur within our domain of influence, yet we protect our sense of personal control and self-efficacy by blaming factors beyond our control. Psychologists call such misattribution the "self-serving bias," and it markedly influences the amount and quality of participation in the analysis of a near hit or injury. As a result, I've suggested elsewhere (Geller 2000a, 2001d) that a behavioral analysis of an incident should start with a discussion of environmental or engineering factors. After a constructive discussion of environment-related causes of an injury, people are more likely to participate

External excuses protect our self-efficacy.

in a frank and open discussion of possible individual or behavioral factors that might have contributed to the incident.

At my psychology of safety seminars, participants list a number of practical ways to increase perceptions of personal control. The most frequent suggestions include:

- Set short-term goals and track achievements.

- Give recognition and corrective feedback for activities that contribute to injury prevention, not just for outcomes like improved injury statistics.

- Provide opportunities for employees to set personal goals, teach peers, and chart their small wins.

- Teach basic behavior-change intervention strategies—especially interpersonal feedback and recognition procedures—to an entire work force.

- Provide workers time and resources to develop, implement, and evaluate intervention programs.

- Show employees how to graph daily records of baseline, intervention, and follow-up data.

- Post graphs of group participation at various safety-related activities.

Optimism

Optimism is reflected in the statement "I expect the best." It's the expectation that life events, including personal actions, will turn out well (Peterson 2000; Scheier and Carver 1985; Seligman 1991). Optimism relates positively to achievement. Professor Martin Seligman (1991) reported, for example, that world-class swimmers who scored high on a measure of optimism recovered from defeat and swam even faster compared to those swimmers who scored low. Following defeat, the pessimistic swimmers swam more slowly.

Compared to pessimists, optimists maintain a sense of humor, perceive problems or challenges in a positive light, and plan for a successful future. *They focus on what they can do rather than on how they feel* (Carver, Scheier, and Weintraub 1989; Sherer et al. 1982; Peterson and Barrett 1987). As a result, optimists handle stressors constructively and experience positive stress rather than negative distress (Scheier, Weintraub, and Carver 1986). Optimists essentially expect to be successful at whatever they do, and so they work harder than pessimists do to reach their goals. As a result, optimists are beneficiaries of a self-fulfilling prophecy (Tavris and Wade 1995). An optimistic perspective can influence one's attempt to achieve more.

Obviously, anything that increases our self-efficacy should increase optimism. Plus, if our personal control is strengthened, we perceive that we have more

Optimists have higher outcome-expectancies.

influence over our consequences. This gives us more reason to expect the best. We perceive our outcome-expectancies as more positive and more likely to occur. Again, we see how the five belief states discussed in this chapter are clearly intertwined and relate to real empowerment. A change in one will likely influence the other four and affect one's sense of empowerment and degree of participation.

In Conclusion

The pop psychologists and motivational speakers are right. Beliefs are important in enabling success or empowerment. However, these advocates usually tell us about only one kind of belief—self-affirmation or self-confidence in one's ability to meet a challenge. Clinical psychologists call this *self-efficacy*.

Self-efficacy is a key to success, but it's not the only key. A belief that a particular action plan will be effective is also critical, as well as a belief that the ultimate outcome of the intervention is worth the effort. Psychologists call the former belief *response-efficacy* and the latter *outcome-expectancy*.

Safety leaders need to understand and appreciate these three types of personal beliefs and attempt to influence them when designing messages to activate participation. Research has shown that messages arousing the fear emotion work if the scare tactic is believable (outcome-expectancy), and if the message includes a straightforward behavioral strategy for avoiding the negative consequence (response-efficacy) and convinces the audience they can successfully use the countermeasure (self-efficacy).

These three beliefs also need to be considered when teaching the steps of a safety improvement process. It's not enough to convince participants they can perform a certain technique (self-efficacy). Participants must also believe the technique will work to produce a desirable outcome (response-efficacy), and that the ultimate effects of the intervention will be worthwhile (outcome-expectancy). Furthermore, participants are more likely to use the tools or methods they are taught if they believe the process will increase their *personal control* and if they are *optimistic* about their ultimate success. Thus, real empowerment is powerful because it includes perceptions of both *personal control* and *optimism*.

Inspiring these five beliefs in yourself and others is key to maximizing participation and success in a safety-improvement process. This chapter covered a few ways of doing this, but many more strategies for facilitating empowerment and fueling *The Participation Factor* for occupational safety are covered in the following chapters. You can learn some unique and creative ways to increase empowerment by first teaching others the five belief states discussed here and then asking the basic question, "What can we do around here to enhance any of these belief states in you with regard to maintaining an injury-free workplace?" Of course, you need to ask and answer this question of yourself first.

3

The Psychology of Nonparticipation

Before solving a problem, we must understand it. This chapter explains why low worker involvement in occupational safety is the norm in many work cultures. Barriers to participating in occupational safety activities are revealed by recounting an outrageous incident that called for intervention but none occurred. People's belief in a just world is introduced as a primary reason that no one helped a teenager in distress and also as a primary explanation for low participation in occupational safety activities. Two decision-making models are presented to account for people's lack of actively caring for others when the need for helpful participation is imminent.

We cracked the surface of *The Participation Factor* in Chapter 1. I stressed putting less focus on the third E-word of traditional safety—enforcement—and provided a rather lengthy rationale. The bottom line is that the enforcement approach obstructs a positive attitude and suppresses proactive communication. The key to preventing occupational injuries is to discuss occurrences of all negative incidents (from near hits and first-aid cases to lost-time injuries and fatalities) with regard to the potential contributing factors (from environmental and engineering influences to social, behavioral, and attitudinal variables). Without such communication from the workers in the field who are potentially at risk for an injury, the most effective prevention interventions cannot be developed and implemented.

Thus, the prevention of occupational injuries requires daily dedicated involvement of all line workers. This calls for another E-word—empowerment—which was the theme of Chapter 2. Here I presented the psychological perspective of empowerment, which includes five person states—self-efficacy, response-efficacy, outcome-expectancy, personal control, and optimism. Enhancing these beliefs or expectancies in people leads to increased feelings of empowerment and more participation in relevant activities. This book is all about increasing the perception of personal empowerment to reduce the occurrence of workplace injuries.

Before we get further into problem-solving techniques, we need to understand the problem: low or less-than-desired participation in safety-related activities designed to prevent occupational injuries. So let's consider the environment-based, behavior-based, and person-based factors contributing to this problem. I've already addressed a primary cause of low participation—the enforcement approach and the accompanying dependency perspective employees adopt with regard to occupational safety. Additional factors contributing to low involvement in safety-related activities can be explored by considering a situation where participation to help another person was clearly called for, but didn't occur.

An Illustrative Anecdote

This story is outrageous but true. It happened at a restaurant in Myrtle Beach, South Carolina, on July 26, 2000. Recall the lesson from Chapter 2 that stories or individual case studies are often the best way to get an audience on board.

Buttercup begins to hassle Anna.

Why? Because the audience can visualize themselves in the same situation and experience the consequences through imagery. That's what I want you to do here. Visualize yourself observing the following circumstances while eating dinner with some close friends from work. Put yourself in the same situation and consider what you would do (if anything) if you were there.

Although advertised as a "fun" place for families, the restaurant is known for its unusual service: the waiters and waitresses wear humorous costumes and heckle patrons while they eat. It's also common for the wait staff to place paper hats—bearing "humorous" or demeaning labels—on customers' heads. Thus, many customers go to this restaurant, one of a chain throughout the United States, ready for mutual verbal harassment with the staff—all in good fun.

This story is about a table of four—mom, dad, their son Joey (age 7), and their 15-year-old niece, Anna (only the names have been changed). After they ordered their meals, the heckling began.

From the start, the 15-year-old was targeted for ridicule. Her waiter, nicknamed Buttercup, first teased her about the small star tattoo on her shoulder. Then he brought out a paper hat labeled "Puberty Stinks" and placed it on her head. Anna calmly took off the hat and placed it on the floor. "What's the matter? Don't you like your hat?" teased Buttercup.

Buttercup pushes a meringue pie into Anna's face.

When Anna ignored this badgering, Buttercup got more intrusive. He took out a black marker and printed a demeaning epithet across Anna's bare back. Some onlookers laughed aloud, and Anna looked quite embarrassed. She did not say a word, though, and continued to eat her meal. She was visibly upset, because her hand shook as she brought food to her mouth.

Seemingly enjoying the public attention for his antics, the waiter wasn't about to give up on getting a visible rise from Anna. He returned from the kitchen with a meringue pie, and you guessed it, he pushed it directly into Anna's face. Well, this was the last straw for Anna. Buttercup got the rise he wanted—literally. The slim 110-pound teenager sprang from her chair—pie filling dripping from her face—and tackled the 6-foot, 200-pound waiter.

After a brief scuffle on the floor, Buttercup stood up, holding Anna by her ankles. Then he carried her outside and dropped her safely in a Dumpster. Anna returned to her table in tears. She was immediately consoled by her aunt, who then accompanied her to the rest room. When the waiter delivered the check, Anna's uncle paid it.

Buttercup gets the last laugh.

Normal Reactions?

If you had been there, what would your reaction have been? When I heard this story, I was initially stunned by the lack of intervention from other diners. I imagined myself standing on a chair and announcing, "Everyone's meals are on the house. Management will gladly cover your food and drink to avoid the million-dollar lawsuit Anna has every right to file!" And I visualized that I would have given this speech as soon as the waiter took a marker to Anna's back. That's when Buttercup crossed the line, right?

How could anyone have let this incident escalate to its outlandish outcome without intervening? I was astounded to learn that Anna's uncle not only paid the check, but also added a significant tip for the waiter who assaulted and embarrassed his niece. When later challenged by Anna's parents, his defense was, "Everything happened so fast."

Hindsight Is 20/20

I'll bet your reaction was similar to mine. You can visualize yourself getting involved to help Anna—right? At the very least, you would not have given the waiter a financial reward. But wait—don't be so sure. A number of factors discouraged other diners from intervening. Similar factors also hinder participation in occupational safety and health activities.

Situations occur every day at work where we could say or do something about an environmental hazard or an at-risk behavior. The behaviors may not be as intentional as Buttercup's, but they put people in danger of being injured just the same.

After a person gets hurt, our hindsight kicks in. "Why wasn't the environmental hazard removed?" "Why didn't someone warn her about being in the line of fire?" "Why wasn't the appropriate protective equipment used?" "Why didn't he ask for help in moving those heavy boxes?"

I'm sure you can recall specific instances where an injury would have been avoided if someone had stepped in or spoken up. So why don't we get involved? Let's consider four barriers that impeded intervention in the restaurant, and see whether they are relevant to industrial settings.

Four Barriers That Impede Intervention

That's the Way It Is. The restaurant is known for hassling its customers. That goes with the territory. If you want a quiet, peaceful dinner, go someplace else. The climate at this establishment invites interpersonal confrontation, from the attire of the staff to the props visibly available for "fun" interactions and practical jokes.

Obviously, we're talking about culture—a factor that is frequently entertained as a critical determinant of an organization's safety performance. Do

Supervisors
should walk
the safety talk.

managers walk the safety talk, or deliver mixed messages? Does a scenario similar to the one depicted above ever happen at your work site?

I've visited many plants where the behaviors of people in leadership positions are not consistent with safety rules and regulations. Once a plant manager introduced me as a consultant with an important safety message and then left the room, presumably headed for more important business. These examples, and many others I'm sure you've experienced, set the stage for compromising safety in the name of efficiency or productivity. In such a work culture, you can expect many opportunities for safety intervention to be overlooked.

Someone Else Will Help. Social psychologists have found that the greater the number of people witnessing an event calling for intervention, the lower the probability that any one person will help (Latané and Darley 1970). A popular explanation for this "bystander apathy effect" is diffusion of responsibility—people assume another onlooker will help. The more observers, the more reasonable it seems to make this assumption.

Given this observation, one possible reason no one intervened to help Anna was the expectation that someone else would intervene. Actually, it's logical to assume that the most appropriate people to intervene on Anna's behalf were those at her table. In fact, onlookers at other tables might have thought they'd be meddling if they offered Anna support. They might even suppose that Buttercup had a special relationship with Anna or her family, and this explained the outrageous behavior.

Have you ever held back from actively caring for safety because you figured someone else would or should help? Maybe you even felt it would be more appropriate for someone closer to the situation to step in. In many work cultures it's natural for individuals to feel this reluctance. Not only might you be intruding, but it's reasonable to think that someone else—a team member or a friend—is in a better position to help.

What Should I Do? What should have been said to Buttercup when he wrote on Anna's back? What feedback should Anna's uncle have given to Buttercup and his manager, perhaps after refusing to pay the check? What should Anna have said to stifle the belittling behavior she found uncomfortable?

Researchers have shown that individuals are more likely to help others in emergency situations when they know what to do (Shotland and Heinold 1985). And naturally, an intervention from people who know what to do is more likely to be effective. Hence, observers without relevant training are quick to defer responsibility to someone else.

Assertiveness training helps people stand up for their rights and come to the realization that their feelings and opinions matter and should be expressed. Such training involves direct instruction and role-playing of specific verbal expressions to use in order to regain control in certain situations. Practicing what to say to resolve or alleviate a conflict beforehand enables people to intervene effectively in the heat of the moment. Likewise, practicing what to say before asking a team member to work more safely will increase the likelihood you'll actually intervene and be effective. Instead of asking, "Why don't you follow the safe operating procedure?" practice asking, "What barriers are holding you back from doing the job as safely as possible?"

When reflecting on a situation in which an intervention was called for but didn't occur, it's a good idea to consider what could have been done to help. Some people's personalities make it particularly difficult for them to stand up for their rights. These individuals are in special need of practicing assertive dialogue. Years ago Steve Roberts, Mike Gilmore, and I supported this contributing factor of personality by finding that those employees at a plastics manufacturing plant in Texas and a textiles manufacturing plant in North Carolina who were naturally more assertive and outgoing, as assessed by a measure of extroversion (Eysenck and Eysenck 1985), stated greater willingness to give their coworkers supportive and corrective feedback for safety-related behaviors (Geller, Roberts, and Gilmore 1996).

Did She Ask for It? Did it ever cross your mind that Anna's reactions, or lack of actions, influenced the series of unpleasant exchanges? In the same vein, have you ever thought the victim of an unpleasant workplace conflict or an injury did something to deserve it? It's common for people to feel that victims of crimes or accidents caused their own fate. Social psychologists call this phenomenon the "just-world hypothesis"—we get what we deserve and we deserve what we get (Lerner 1980).

Consider how this belief can be a barrier to helping others. Most observers of the confrontation between Buttercup and Anna were not privy to the verbal interactions that preceded and accompanied the successively more aggressive encounters. They derived their own explanations for the incident, and given the just-world bias, many probably blamed Anna for her misfortune. Such bias provides a convenient excuse for not helping someone.

Can this bias be a barrier for safety-related intervention? Have you ever observed at-risk behavior and said to yourself something like, "What a dumb thing to do; if he gets hurt he deserves it." This kind of mental script reflects the just-world hypothesis and offers one more reason for not intervening on behalf of another person's safety or health. Let's examine this phenomenon more closely and see how it can affect participation in safety-related activities.

It's Not Safe to Believe in a Just World

First, realize that it's not unusual to blame the victim of unfortunate circumstances. Psychological research has shown that victims of kidnapping, rape, and assault are often asked what they did to bring on the misfortune (McCaul et al. 1990). For example, many people believe rape victims are somewhat to blame for their rapes. "If she hadn't dressed and acted that way, she would not have been sexually assaulted." In other research, battered wives were viewed by some as being responsible for their abusive husbands' behavior (Summers and Feldman 1984; Kristiansen and Giulietti 1990).

Why does this absurd interpretation occur? Social psychologists believe this thinking is a form of self-defense that helps us maintain our belief that life is safe, orderly, and predictable (Aronson, Wilson, and Akert 1998). In other words, by believing that victims do things to bring on their afflictions, we feel safer. If life were unfair and random, then innocent people like ourselves could also be victimized and injured.

Belief in a Just World

As I mentioned above, this bias is referred to as the "just-world hypothesis" (Lerner 1980). It is reflected in common slogans like "What goes around comes around" and "Everything happens for a reason."

It's hard to deny that bad things happen in life. Pick up any newspaper and you can read about people enduring terrible misfortunes every day. This is certainly disturbing and can cause significant distress. How do we deal

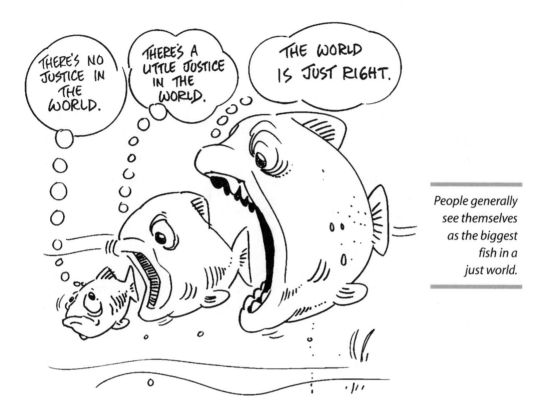

People generally see themselves as the biggest fish in a just world.

with the constant reminder that tragedies not only happen, but are also relatively common? One way is to believe in a just world.

Bad things happen to bad people and good things happen to good people. Since most of us see ourselves as decent and basically good, bad things won't happen to us. We see ourselves as the largest fish (see illustration above). In the eyes of the beholder, a just world is a safe world. However, this attributional defense mechanism does have some unfortunate ramifications for industrial health and safety. Let's consider four ways this defense mechanism can hinder participation in efforts to protect workers on the job.

Increased Risk-Taking. The phrase "It won't happen to me" is familiar to all of us. It reflects a common and functional assumption. If people thought they'd be injured at work on a particular day, they wouldn't go to work—right? So this belief enables us to face situations where a serious injury is possible—from the drive to and from work to numerous situations in between. As it turns out, on most days this conviction is supported. Nothing happens to us. If someone gets hurt, it's the other guy.

This belief, obviously consistent with the just-world hypothesis, increases risk-taking. We've all been there. We take a chance—a calculated risk—because we think we're safe and secure in a just world.

Maybe we wouldn't take as many risks if we realized that our coworkers who have suffered injuries also believed in a just world. They didn't expect anything bad to happen to them—only to the other guy. Now they know what it's like to be that other guy. Perhaps they now believe a "just world" implies that we should do everything we can to reduce the possibility of injury to ourselves and to others.

Superficial Incident Analysis. If we believe people get what they deserve in life, then they deserve any injury they receive. It sounds horrible and we would never say something like this aloud. But let's be honest—haven't you at one time or another tried to feel better about someone getting hurt or killed by looking for things the victim could have done to prevent the incident? Do you feel more sympathy for the passengers than the driver killed in a vehicle crash?

We feel safer when we can somehow blame the victim of misfortune. Then the tragedy does not seem so tragic. After all, if she had done this or that she wouldn't have been injured. We feel more secure knowing we could prevent such adversity from happening to us by doing what the victim didn't do.

Recognizing that individual action can cause or prevent injury is not bad, but the actual or potential behaviors of a victim do not tell the whole story. They only represent a portion of the facts—not the fault. The analysis obviously can't stop here, but sometimes it does, and for this we can blame our belief in a just world.

Low Participation. Have you ever thought safety is personal? Does it seem more natural or comfortable to give coworkers corrective feedback about their production-related behaviors than their safety-related behaviors? Why is this so often the case? Why do people's production-related activities fall within our domain of interpersonal influence, but their safety-related behaviors do not?

Answers to these questions are determined by our personal beliefs and biases. Through education, training, and intervention programs, some work cultures have, in fact, improved their safety performance dramatically by making safety as impersonal as productivity. In these work settings, it's just as natural to intervene on behalf of someone's safety as it is on behalf of product quality.

But this doesn't happen overnight. It's not easy to get people to actively care for other people's safety. Not only must they know what to do, they must also feel comfortable intervening and believe it's the right thing to do. We might be less likely to step in or speak up if we believe people simply get what they deserve. Why should we bother?

Well, you can also believe it's your responsibility to help make the world just and equitable by intervening to make it safer. This includes removing environmental hazards and barriers to safe behavior as well as helping others to become more mindful of behaviors that put themselves and others at risk.

Lack of Public Support. Researchers of risk perception and communication have found that the public concern following disastrous events is relatively low when the victims are perceived as gaining something (Sandman 1991; Slovic 1991). For example, when individuals are injured while taking risks in order to increase production, the public perception is typically, "They got what they deserved." In these cases, it's difficult to obtain public sympathy and financial support for efforts to make the situation safer.

On the other hand, when hazards and injuries seem unfair, as when a child is molested or inflicted with a deadly disease, the public is sympathetic. Therefore, it's comparatively easy to obtain contributions or voluntary assistance for programs that target vulnerable populations, like physically challenged individuals or learning-disabled children.

The victims of workplace injuries are not viewed as weak and defenseless. Occupational injuries are indiscriminately distributed among employees who take risks, and the just-world perception is that they get what they deserve. This helps explain the low public and political support for agencies like OSHA (Occupational Safety and Health Administration), MSHA (Mine Safety and Health Administration), and NIOSH (National Institute for Occupational Safety and Health) that are charged with protecting employees.

More lives of productive Americans are lost in occupational mishaps and vehicle crashes than from cancer and heart attacks combined (National Safety Council 1998). Yet the amount of government support for cancer and cardiovascular disease is many times greater than the amount allocated for research and intervention to prevent injuries and fatalities in the workplace and on the road. I believe the just-world hypothesis is partly responsible for this unjust situation.

What to Do

So what can we do about the just-world hypothesis and its impact on workplace safety? Understanding the just-world hypothesis and its implications does nothing to help the problem, at least on the surface. But suppose we can alter this belief a little and turn it in our favor. Through education and daily conversations, we can convince people that a just world actually depends on our participation. We can make our world safer and more just by doing our part to remove environmental hazards, design refinements to make equipment more user friendly, and help people improve their safety-related behavior. Bottom line: A just world can be an ultimate vision made possible by our attempts to actively care for the safety and health of ourselves and our coworkers.

Deciding Not to Participate

This chapter began with a description of an extraordinary series of encounters in a restaurant that warranted helpful intervention from any of a number of onlookers. I introduced four barriers that prevented the victim from receiving help from fellow diners and linked each to the problem of low participation in occupational safety. Now let's examine these barriers to participation in the context of the onlookers' information processing and decision making. This will enable further understanding of the nonparticipation problem. Awareness of the reasons or excuses people have for not helping others could suggest ways to fuel *The Participation Factor* for occupational safety.

As a result of their seminal research, Latané and Darley (1970) proposed that an observer makes four sequential decisions before helping a victim. These four decisions (depicted in Figure 3.1) are influenced by 1) the situation or environmental context in which a helping opportunity occurs, 2) the nature of the crisis, 3) the presence of other bystanders and their reactions, and 4) relevant social norms and rules.

Although the model was developed to evaluate intervention in situations like the restaurant scenario—where there is need for direct and reactive intervention—it is relevant to proactive participation to prevent workplace injuries.

Step 1: Is Something Wrong?

The first step in deciding whether to intervene is simply noticing that something is wrong. Some situations or events naturally attract more attention than others. Many patrons of the restaurant might not even have noticed the conflict between Buttercup and Anna. The interactions at their own table, including ordering or eating food, could have blocked their attention to other happenings in the restaurant. Likewise, in active and noisy work environments, people narrow their focus to what is personally relevant. They learn to tune out irrelevant stimuli.

If stimulus overload can affect people's attention to an emergency, it can certainly reduce attention to common everyday situations that are inconspicuous, but nevertheless require helpful participation. Consider, for example, the various needs for proactive behavior that can prevent an injury. Environmental hazards are easy to overlook, especially in a busy and noisy workplace requiring focused attention on a demanding task. Even less noticeable and attention-getting are the safe or at-risk behaviors of other people. Yet these behaviors need proactive support or correction, as in the safety coaching approach mentioned in Chapter 2.

Even if a need for proactive participation is noticed, an observer will not necessarily get involved. The bystander must interpret the situation as requiring his or her help. This leads us to the next question that is answered before deciding to participate.

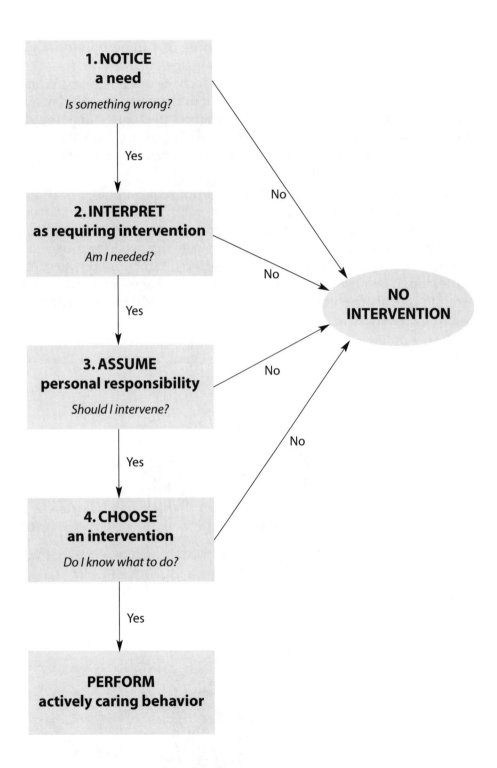

Figure 3.1 Participation for occupational safety involves four sequential decisions.

Step 2: Am I Needed?

As shown in the illustration below, people can come up with a variety of excuses for not helping someone. Distress cues, such as cries for help and the actions of other observers, can clarify an event as an emergency. When people are confused, they look to other people for information and guidance. In other words, by watching what others are doing, people figure out how to interpret an ambiguous event and how to react to it. Therefore, the behavior of others is especially important when stimulus cues are not present to clarify that a situation requires intervention.

In the restaurant situation, Anna did not request help, nor did others at Anna's table give distress signals. In fact, some facial expressions of the spectators closest to the conflict may have suggested they were actually enjoying Buttercup's hassling. Now, in the workplace, the need for proactive participation is rarely as obvious as the negative interaction between Anna and Buttercup. If conflict like that occurred in a work environment, many people would probably react in a hurry. Such events would be noticeable and likely interpreted as needing attention.

But would you assume personal responsibility and respond? Many bystanders in the restaurant noticed the event, and some of these observers

Many excuses are available for not participating.

probably interpreted it as warranting intervention. Thus, Steps 1 and 2 of Latané and Darley's decision model were probably satisfied. If so, a breakdown might occur at Step 3—perceiving personal responsibility.

Step 3: Should I Intervene?

In this stage you ask yourself, "Is it *my* responsibility to intervene?" The answer would be obvious if you were the only witness to a situation you perceive as an emergency. But you might not answer "yes" to this question when you know other people are observing the same emergency or safety hazard. In this case, you have reason to believe someone else will intervene, perhaps a person more capable than you. This perception relieves you of personal responsibility.

A breakdown at this stage of the decision model doesn't mean the observers don't care about the welfare of the victim. Actually, they might care very much about the victim, but they defer responsibility to others they feel are more appropriate or better qualified to intervene. In the restaurant example, other diners may have felt that Anna's aunt or uncle should intervene.

Similarly, employees might care a great deal about the safety and health of their coworkers, but feel relatively incapable of acting on their caring. People might resist taking personal responsibility to actively care because they don't believe they have the most effective tools to make a difference. They don't feel empowered. I'm sure you see the connection to the self-efficacy and response-efficacy lessons of Chapter 2.

In addition to having a "can-do" attitude, people need to believe it's their personal responsibility to get involved. In many work situations, it's easy to assume safety is the responsibility of someone else—the safety director or a team safety captain. After all, these individuals have "safety" in their job titles, and they meet regularly to discuss safety issues. They even get to go off site now and then to attend a safety conference—where they learn the techniques that make them the most capable to intervene. So it's their responsibility.

The challenge in achieving an injury-free workplace is to convince everyone they have a personal responsibility to intervene for safety. Indeed, a social norm or expectancy must be established that everyone shares equally in a daily assignment to keep everyone safe and healthy. Furthermore, safety leaders or captains need to accept the special responsibility of teaching others any techniques they learn at conferences or group meetings that could increase perceived competence (or self-efficacy) to participate effectively.

All this is easier said than done, of course. But if we don't meet this challenge, many people are likely to decide that participating in safety activities is not for them. They could feel this way even after viewing an obvious at-risk behavior or a condition that would benefit from their immediate action.

Step 4: Do I Know What to Do?

This last step of Latané and Darley's decision model points out the importance of education and training. Education gives people the rationale and principles behind a particular intervention approach. It gives people information for designing or refining intervention strategies, enabling a sense of ownership for the particular tools they help to develop. Through training, people learn how to translate principles and rules into specific behaviors or intervention strategies. As I discussed in Chapter 2, for example, training in safety coaching should include role-playing exercises so people can practice communication techniques and receive specific feedback regarding their strengths and weaknesses. The bottom line here is that people who learn how to intervene effectively through relevant education and training are more likely to participate when the need arises (Clark and Word 1974; Shotland and Heinold 1985).

A Consequence Analysis of Participation

Now let's consider another approach to understanding the problem of low participation in occupational safety. Since behavior is motivated by consequences (or outcome-expectancies), a person's decision to actively care can be analyzed according to the perceived positive versus negative consequences one expects to receive. A consequence analysis can be applied to almost everything we do. The result is a risk/benefit ratio for participating.

If people are motivated to maximize positive consequences and minimize negative consequences, participation will occur only if the perceived benefits outweigh the perceived costs. In other words, the cost/benefit ratio must be less than one. This framework suggests strategies for increasing participation that Latané and Darley's sequential decision-making model does not inspire.

According to an interpretation based on the power of consequences, restaurant patrons who saw the negative encounter between Anna and Buttercup resisted taking responsibility because they perceived that it could mean more trouble—or embarrassment—than it was worth. It was safer to assume that someone else more capable would intervene. According to this consequence model, people hesitated to help Anna because they perceived more potential costs than benefits, not because they were apathetic or failed to interpret a need to take personal responsibility.

Dr. Jane Piliavin and colleagues (1981) developed a cost-benefit model to interpret people's propensity to help others in various crisis situations. Two basic categories of potential negative consequences for helping are personal costs, including effort, inconvenience, potential injury, and humiliation; and costs to the victim if no intervention occurs. This latter category includes two subcategories: the personal costs of not helping, including criticism, guilt, or shame; and empathic costs from internalizing the victim's distress and physical needs. The authors combined these negative consequences for getting involved and for not getting involved in order to predict whether participation will occur under particular circumstances.

The matrix in Figure 3.2 combines two levels of cost (low and high) to the potential participant and the victim in order to predict when actively caring behavior will occur. Participation is most likely (lower left cell of Figure 3.2) when the costs for helping are low—for example, convenient and not dangerous—and potential costs to the victim for not helping are high—as when the victim is seriously injured. On the other hand, intervention is least likely when the perceived personal costs for intervening are high—for example, inconvenient and risky—and the apparent potential costs to the victim for not intervening are low—as when an experienced worker is performing at-risk behavior with no negative consequences.

The Anna/Buttercup incident fits the lower right cell of Figure 3.2—relatively high perceived costs for both helper and victim. This means significant conflict for the potential helper. The conflict can be resolved by presuming someone else will intervene—diffusion of responsibility—or perhaps by rationalizing that the person does not deserve help, as suggested by the just-world hypothesis.

Most voluntary behavior can be viewed in terms of a risk/benefit ratio.

Costs to Bystander for Intervening

		Low	High
Costs to Victim	*Low*	Depends on person factors	Intervention improbable
If Bystander Does Not Intervene	*High*	Intervention probable	Diffusion of responsibility

Figure 3.2 The probability of participation is determined by the costs to a bystander for intervening and the costs to the victim if the bystander does not intervene.

The upper left quadrant of Figure 3.2 represents situations most analogous to participating in injury prevention. Although a simple, low-cost intervention might be called for to correct an environmental hazard or an at-risk behavior, there is no immediate emergency and thus no need for immediate action. There is low perceived cost if no action is taken: "We've been working under these conditions for months and no one has been hurt." Piliavin et al. (1981) advise that intervention in situations represented by this cost quadrant is most difficult to predict. Many factors can influence the extent to which consequences are viewed as positive or negative, and small changes in these factors can tilt the cost-reward balance in favor of stepping in or standing back.

Through testimonials and constructive discussions, employees can be convinced the potential cost of not intervening is higher than they initially thought. This can occur, for example, by considering the large degree of plant-wide exposure to a certain uncorrected hazard. Also, it might be worthwhile to remind people of the widespread detrimental learning that could occur from the continued performance of risky behavior. Furthermore, education and role-playing exercises can reduce the perceived personal costs of participating. It's also true that person-based factors, such as the beliefs and expectancies discussed in Chapter 2, determine whether the individual gets involved.

Although the matrix in Figure 3.2 focuses entirely on negative consequences, it's important to consider that positive consequences can also play a prominent role in determining one's decision to get involved. In occupational safety, for example, proactive participation in safety can not only prevent a serious injury, it also sets the right example for others to follow. It can also increase certain positive feeling states in both those who give and those who receive the caring behavior. This in turn increases the probability of future proactive participation for safety by both individuals.

In Conclusion

This chapter used a seemingly outrageous incident at a restaurant to set the stage for a discussion of barriers to participation. Four aspects of the restaurant scenario were barriers that contributed to Anna's plight:

- Interpersonal confrontation was expected in this milieu.

- The high number of observers made it easy to shirk personal responsibility.

- A suitable action plan was not readily available.

- The victim probably did something to deserve her punishing treatment.

I hope you see the relevance of these four barriers to safety-related participation. Obviously, the work culture determines whether interpersonal intervention is viewed as actively caring or as meddling. A number of additional factors identified throughout this book influence whether people feel comfortable intervening when surrounded by other coworkers who could also help. Education and training programs affect whether an effective intervention strategy is even available.

The fourth barrier to safety-related participation reflects the "just-world hypothesis"—a common-sense belief that the world is fair and people get what they deserve. This viewpoint has several ramifications for safety, including:

- It lowers the perception of personal risk among those who believe they are basically good—which covers most of us.

- It contributes to victim blaming and inhibits intervention for safety.

- It's responsible, in part, for the low budgets of governmental agencies that target occupational safety.

This chapter also analyzed the problem of low participation in occupational safety with two decision-making models developed through rigorous research. The schema developed by Latané and Darley (1970) proposes that we answer four successive questions before helping someone in need:

1. Is something wrong?

2. Am I needed?

3. Should I intervene?

4. Do I know what to do?

This decision logic suggests certain methods for increasing participation. Specifically, this model supports the need to teach employees how to recognize and correct environmental hazards and at-risk behaviors. It is also imperative to promote safety as a core value of the organization. This means everyone assumes responsibility for safety and never waits for someone else to act.

A consequence—or cost/benefit—model offers more guidance for bene-fiting *The Participation Factor.* It enables us to consider motivational aspects of a person's decision to get involved. Conditions that decrease perceptions of personal costs to the potential helper (for participating) and increase percep-tions of costs to victims (if the potential helper does not participate) make participation more likely. In addition, it's useful to help people realize the potential positive consequences or rewards available to both the giver and the receiver of actively caring behavior. When the perceived internal and external rewards for participating outweigh the rewards for doing nothing, people will probably get involved.

Most situations involve relatively low costs and rewards to both the deliv-erer and receiver of safety-related participation. Although the costs to an individual for helping may be low, the recipient of a proactive safety inter-vention is only a potential victim, so the perceived cost for not helping is also low. Education and training can reduce these perceived costs to the interven-tion agent and increase the perceived costs to potential victims. The result: more frequent, actively caring participation in occupational safety. Education and training, however, are not sufficient for the amount of safety-related par-ticipation needed to attain and sustain an injury-free workplace. The remaining chapters describe additional ways to develop and support *The Participation Factor* and thus get more people involved in occupational safety.

The Benefits of Self-Persuasion

Long-term participation in occupational safety requires self-persuasion and self-direction. External accountability systems, including threats of penalties and promises of rewards, provide insufficient fuel for The Participation Factor. *This chapter takes us beyond these motivational schemes found in both traditional and behavior-based approaches to industrial safety. In other words, holding people accountable for their safety involvement only gets you so far. The highest level of safety excellence occurs when people feel responsible and self-accountable for safety-related participation. This chapter shows you how to get there by explaining relevant research-based principles from cognitive and social psychology.*

Behavior-based safety has contributed significantly to increased employee participation in occupational safety. The basic principles and procedures of behavior-based safety are given in several other sources (e.g., Geller 1998b; 2001e; Krause, Hidley, and Hodson 1996; McSween 1995; Sulzer-Azaroff 1998), and the effectiveness of this approach at reducing workplace injuries is also well documented in the research literature (e.g, see reviews in Geller 2001d and Petersen 1989). However, some descriptions and applications of behavior-based safety are narrow and less than ideal. This has led to substantial controversy and confusion regarding the behavior-based approach to increasing participation in occupational safety (Geller 1999, 2001f).

Some have argued that a behavioral focus puts excessive responsibility on the worker and gives managers an excuse to shirk their safety responsibilities (Frederick and Howe 2001; Howe 1998; Hoyle 1998; Manuel 1998). Others claim the behavioral approach is too limiting and should be abandoned for a more holistic or culture-focused approach (Simon 2001;

Topf 1998, 2001). Still others have recognized the usefulness of behavior-based safety, but have appealed for breakthroughs, including more efficiency, flexibility, and effectiveness with regard to producing long-term change (Kamp 2001; Sarkus 2001).

This book is not about behavior-based safety, but participation *is* behavior. So this book does focus on behavior and practical ways to increase the quantity and quality of behavior as it relates to *The Participation Factor* for occupational safety. However, the tools and methods presented here have been gleaned from the entire field of psychology, including the cognitive, social, and behavioral disciplines. Thus, this book addresses the concerns of safety professionals who call for a broader perspective than that of behavior-based safety.

This chapter exemplifies a broad coverage of the human dynamics of safety involvement. It draws specifically from cognitive and social psychology, and describes research-based principles and procedures omitted from the standard books on applied behavior analysis and behavior-based safety. While none of this research-tested material contradicts behavior-based safety, explanations and interpretations of empirical findings require us to go beyond the typical education and training in applied behavior analysis. For example, the theme of this chapter—self-persuasion—is not covered in behavior-based safety books, articles, or workshops.

Participation and Self-Perception

We begin with a basic premise in behavioral science that supports the need to get people more involved in safety-related activities. This is the principle behind the common slogan in behavior-based safety that it's possible to "act a person into safe thinking" (Geller 2001d, p. 18). I'll show later in this chapter, however, that the method used to direct or motivate behavior determines how much thinking or attitude change follows the participation and how long the participation will continue.

First, let's consider the extent to which our behaviors designate who we think we are. The notion that we define who we are from our behavior is founded in the teaching and research of B. F. Skinner (1953) and the follow-up scholarship of Daryl J. Bem (1972). Dr. Bem developed a comprehensive theory of self-perception on the basic premise that "individuals come to 'know' their own attitudes, emotions, and other internal states partially by inferring them from observations of their own overt behavior and/or the circumstances in which this behavior occurs" (p. 2). Of course these perceptions can be inaccurate, as illustrated on the next page.

When we want to learn what another person is thinking or feeling, we look to see how that person acts in a particular environmental context.

Similarly, according to Bem's self-perception theory, when we want to know how *we* feel, we look at our own behavior and the circumstances surrounding it. This is exemplified by a person eating an excessive amount of food and then stating, "I must have been hungrier than I thought." Or, how about the individual who performs a certain task below par and concludes, "I'm not as good at this as I thought I was." Then there's the employee who goes out of her way to help a coworker and thinks, "I must care more than I thought I did." These are obvious cases of behavior influencing thought processes.

Supportive Research

Classic research by Stanley Schachter and Jerome Singer (1962) supports the claim that self-perception is determined in part by overt behavior. Research subjects were given injections of epinephrine or adrenaline, which made them feel physically aroused. Then these subjects waited individually with one other person who presumably had received the same injection. Moments later the experimenter returned and asked the two individuals to complete a questionnaire about their feelings.

What emotions did these subjects experience? The physiological arousal was the same for every subject, but some reported extreme anger while others said they were very happy. What made the difference? The subject's own behavior and that of the other person in the waiting room, who was actually a research assistant, determined whether the participant felt extreme anger or joy.

The research assistant, posing as another subject, acted in one of two ways during the waiting period. In the Euphoric condition, depicted below, he threw paper airplanes, shot crumpled balls of paper into a wastebasket, and twirled in a hula hoop. He encouraged the subject to join in the fun, and many did.

In the Anger condition, both individuals were asked to complete a questionnaire while waiting for the experimenter to return. The questions were intimate and quite inappropriate, especially the question "With how many men has your mother had extramarital affairs—four and under, five to nine, or ten and over?" When the research assistant read this question he ripped up his survey form in a fit of rage, as illustrated on the next page.

Euphoric behavior caused euphoria.

Perhaps the finding that behavior influenced emotions in this study seems obvious, or just common sense. Realize, however, what the results mean. The participants' emotional reactions were determined by the behavior they observed in themselves and another person. After being physically aroused, they felt joy or anger, depending on external circumstances and accompanying behavior.

Actually, this is only one example of numerous experiments that have demonstrated the crucial role of external events and behaviors on people's perceptions of their emotions, attitudes, and moods. For example, in one series of studies, participants' emotions were manipulated by giving them false auditory feedback about their heartbeat (Valins 1966). When they heard what they thought was their heart beating faster, they felt more sexually aroused or fearful, depending on other external events. Thus, it's possible to change self-perception by altering external conditions. In other words, we can act ourselves (and others) into thinking or feeling a certain way.

Acting People into Certain Ways of Thinking

Suppose you wanted to motivate someone to participate in a particular safety-related activity. How would you do it? Well, even if you believe people can only truly motivate themselves (that is, they can't be motivated by external forces), you can at least establish external conditions or environmental contexts that facilitate intrapersonal motivation. What does this mean? It means you can do things to increase the likelihood that people will do what you want.

Angry behavior caused anger.

Attempts to make this happen are called interventions, and they can vary from developing an external accountability system or incentive program to initiating opportunities for personal choice, ownership, or constructive interpersonal conversation.

The most efficient way to motivate actions in others is to create an environmental context or behavior-consequence relationship that facilitates the occurrence of the desired action—that is, do this behavior and you will get this consequence. In other words, you establish the conditions for people to act themselves into new ways of thinking. Their new behavior can influence a new way of perceiving themselves. This can lead to a new personal label and then to more behavior consistent with that label. "I'm wearing my safety glasses, so I'm a safe worker and should also use all other personal protective equipment."

Thus, personal development can be viewed as a continuous spiral of behavior causing thinking, thinking inducing more behavior, and then this additional behavior influencing more thinking consistent with the behavior, and so on. It doesn't matter which came first—behavior or thinking. What matters is that we can affect beneficial change in others by focusing on their behavior. Then, when people see themselves doing what you want, they *might* change how they view themselves. They *might* act themselves into thinking differently, and thus motivate themselves to sustain the new behavior.

I emphasized "might" in the prior two sentences because some interventions to change behavior do not facilitate an attendant change in thinking. Not all behavior change leads to relevant and supportive change in thinking and self-perception. Let's consider some research-based principles for increasing the likelihood that an intervention to increase participation will also influence thinking consistent with the participation, which in turn will help sustain the participation.

Direct versus Indirect Persuasion

Advertisers use direct persuasion. They show us people enjoying positive consequences or avoiding negative consequences by using their products. As such, they apply the "ABC" principle of behavior-based safety to sell their wares or services. The *activator* ("A") announces the availability of a reinforcing *consequence* ("C") if the purchasing *behavior* is performed ("B").

Advertisers also apply research-based principles from social psychology to make their messages more persuasive. Specifically, social scientists have shown the advantages of using highly credible communicators and arousing their audience's emotions (Aronson 1999; Horowitz 1972; Hovland and Weiss 1951). Therefore, sales pitches are often given by authority figures who attempt to get viewers emotionally charged with product-related issues.

Advertisers use the ABC principle to persuade shoppers to buy their products.

Limitations of Direct Persuasion

The direct persuasion of advertisements does not typically ask for behavior that is inconvenient or difficult. Normally, the purpose of an advertisement is to persuade a consumer to select a certain brand of merchandise. This boils down to merely choosing one commodity over another at the retail store, as illustrated above. While shopping, consumers need only to move their hands a few inches to select one product over another. This is hardly a burdensome change in lifestyle. It is not even considered "participation."

Safety-related behavior is usually more inconvenient and requires more effort than switching brands at a supermarket. It often requires significant adjustment in a highly practiced and regular routine at work, at home, or on the road. Thus, adopting a safe way of doing something might first require the elimination of an efficient and convenient at-risk habit. Furthermore, participation in a safety-promotion effort usually requires the regular performance of several inconvenient safety-related behaviors.

Here's my point: Long-term participation in a safety-related work process is far more cumbersome and lifestyle-changing than the consumer behavior targeted by advertisers. As a result, direct persuasion is frequently not the way to increase safety-related behavior or promote long-term participation in a safety process.

Direct attempts to persuade people to make inconvenient changes in their lifestyle often yield disappointing outcomes. For example, communication strategies designed to persuade smokers to quit smoking (Elder, Geller, Hovell, and Mayer 1994), drivers to stop speeding (Geller 1998a), homeowners to conserve water (Geller, Erikson, and Buttram 1983) or insulate their water heaters (Geller 1981), bigoted individuals to cease prejudicial behavior or sexually active people to use condoms (Aronson 1999) have generally been unsuccessful. Similarly, the "Just Say No to Drugs" campaigns have not influenced much behavior change.

The problem with direct persuasion is that it comes across as someone else's idea. It could even give the impression the behavior is actually for someone other than the performer. This can cause a disconnection between the behavior and self-perception. There is no self-persuasion—the state or mindset needed for lasting change.

Advantages of an Indirect Approach

Self-persuasion is more likely to occur when the motivational strategy is less obvious. Have you ever received flattery or a favor from someone and thought, "That person is only trying to get something from me?" In this case, your self-perception will not change, because you're suspicious of the other person's intentions. You might think, "She doesn't really mean that, she's only trying to win my favor." My students use the term "kissing up" for this kind of behavior. And, as depicted in the illustration on the next page, this behavior is not unfamiliar to many parents.

Compliments regarding a person's performance are often more powerful when they are more indirect than direct (Allen 1990; Geller 1997a). Your personal experience probably verifies this. Consider that you overhear a person tell someone else about your superb achievement on a particular assignment. Or, suppose a friend gives you secondhand recognition by sharing what another person said about your special talents. Both of these situations reflect indirect commendation, and would likely have more influence on your self-

Firsthand recognition can seem insincere.

perception than a direct interpersonal statement of praise. Why? Because, the direct approach is tainted by the possibility the flattery is given for an ulterior motive.

Indirect persuasion deviates significantly from the standard direct and top-down method of attempting to obtain compliance with safety regulations. Both approaches might be equally effective at motivating behavior change, but the indirect approach will be far more successful at enhancing the kind of internal dialogue needed to maintain participation in the absence of an external motivator or accountability system.

Creating interventions that can make this happen is not easy, but start by asking yourself, "Does the situation promote individual choice, ownership, and personal accountability?" "Does the context in which safety participation is desired contribute to connecting or disconnecting the link between what people do and what they think of themselves?" "Are the safety-related activities only behaviors or do they stimulate supportive mental scripts or self-persuasion?"

Self-Directed versus Other-Directed Behavior

As discussed above, behavior can be directed from inside a person rather than from observable external factors. Watson and Tharp (1997) refer to such behavior as self-directed, as opposed to other-directed behavior, and point out that self-management strategies require behavior to be self-directed.

Most work-related behavior starts out as other-directed, in the sense that employees follow someone else's instructions. Such direction can come from a training program, an operations manual, or a policy statement. After we learn what to do, essentially by memorizing or internalizing the appropriate instructions, our behavior enters the self-directed stage. In other words, we talk to ourselves or formulate an image before performing a behavior in order to activate the right response. Sometimes we talk to ourselves after performing a behavior in order to reassure ourselves we performed correctly or to figure out ways to do better next time. At this point we're usually open to corrective feedback if it's delivered well.

I use the other-directed versus self-directed distinction to discriminate between accountability and responsibility (Geller 2001b). People often use these words interchangeably. Whether you hold someone accountable or responsible for getting something done, you mean the same thing. You want that person to accomplish a certain task, and you intend to make sure it happens. However, let's consider the receiving end of this situation. How does a person feel about an assignment—does she or he feel *accountable* or *responsible*? Here's where a distinction is evident.

When you are held accountable, you are asked to reach a certain objective or goal, often within a designated time period. But you might not feel personally obligated to meet the deadline. Sometimes the obvious external control can de-motivate participation, as illustrated on the next page. Or, you might feel responsible enough to complete the assignment, but that's all. You do only what's required and no more. In this case, accountability is the same as responsibility.

There are times, however, when you extend your responsibility beyond accountability. You do more than what's required. You coach a coworker on safe operating procedures, or you find the proper PPE for an employee in need of such protection. You go beyond the call of duty as defined by a particular accountability system. This is often essential when it comes to long-term participation in occupational safety. When change agents (such as teachers, work supervisors, or police officers) are not available to hold people accountable, and external programs are not in place to support desired behavior, continued participation requires a transition from other-directed to self-directed. This brings us back to the concept of self-persuasion.

External control can de-motivate participation.

Self-Persuasion and Participation

I define self-persuasion as an internal dialogue or mental script that supports our ongoing behavior and motivates continued participation in the absence of external controls. Such behavior is self-directed (as opposed to other-directed) and self-motivated. Self-directed behavior is more likely than other-directed behavior to influence self-perception, and in turn help to sustain participation.

Obviously, when it comes to injury prevention, self-directed behavior is more desirable than other-directed behavior, because self-directed individuals choose the safe way even when they perform alone. Consequently, it's important to create situations and conditions that promote self-persuasion and a transition from other-directed to self-directed behavior.

Let's consider the impact of certain intervention approaches on self-persuasion and self-directed behavior. Behavioral research suggests that some standard ways of promoting safe work practices leave much to be desired. That is, they hinder self-persuasion, self-directed behavior, and enduring participation in safety-related activities.

Large Incentives Can Hinder Self-Persuasion

Consider that someone offers you a large sum of money—an incentive—to do something to promote safety. While the chance you'll perform the desired activity will increase, the incentive is apt to stifle self-persuasion and a self-directed state. You will be less likely to persuade yourself that the behavior is a reflection of your personal values than if you performed the safety-related behavior for little or no external incentive.

The situation outlined above has been evaluated in numerous psychology experiments, and results have demonstrated the superior influence of small over large incentives. The classic study in this domain was conducted by Leon Festinger and Merrill Carlsmith in 1959. They paid college students either $20 or $1 to tell another student a boring task they had just performed was actually fun. Afterwards, they were asked to offer their personal opinion of the task.

Which group was more likely to develop a self-perception consistent with their verbal behavior? In other words, which incentive influenced more self-persuasion that the task was not as boring as it seemed? Yes, the lower incentive facilitated more self-persuasion, presumably because these subjects had less external motive to call a dull task fun. As a result, they provided themselves internal motivation or justification for their verbal behavior. With only minimal incentive to tell a lie, they convinced themselves the task was really not that boring. In contrast, the $20 group had an excuse for lying and thus did not need to change their perceptions of the task.

The same kind of self-persuasion occurs when we put a lot of effort into a special assignment without extra compensation. Without an external reward for our behavior, we move inside our heads for justification. We persuade ourselves the effort is especially worthwhile and deserves our "blood, sweat, and tears." Analogously, the more inconvenience or discomfort we must go through to join a group (as in the infamous fraternity "Hell Week"), the more self-persuasion will occur to convince ourselves it was worth it. Research by Eliot Aronson and Judson Mills (1959) supports this conclusion. They found that students who went through a severe initiation to become a member of a "special" discussion group rated the group's silly and boring discussion as significantly more interesting than did students who gained admission to the same group with only a mild initiation.

What's the message here for using incentives to motivate safe work practices? Most obviously, safety incentives must not be presented or perceived as a payoff for behavior (Geller 1996). When the only justification people give for their behaviors is external consequences, they are not likely to develop an internal rationale for their actions. Thus, behavior-based rewards for safety should be given only as "tokens of appreciation" for the many things people do to keep themselves and others injury-free. Preventing injury is the big payoff, and that warrants plenty of internal justification or self-persuasion.

Severe Threats Hinder Self-Persuasion

Now let's consider the use of disincentives or threats to motivate behavior. Should a threat be severe or mild? You know the answer to this question. If you want self-persuasion to occur along with with the desired behavior, you should use the smallest disincentive possible to initiate the behavior you want.

Then, through self-persuasion, the behavior has a chance of continuing when the intervention is no longer available.

The superiority of a small over a large disincentive to prevent undesirable behavior was demonstrated in a series of experiments referred to as "the forbidden toy studies" (e.g., Aronson and Carlsmith 1963; Freedman 1965). Children were asked not to play with an attractive toy and then were given either a mild or a severe threat of punishment for disobeying.

In the Mild Threat condition the experimenter said something like, "It is wrong to play with that toy." A statement was added in the Severe Threat condition, such as, "If you play with that toy, I shall be very angry and will have to do something about it." Then, the experimenter left the room and stepped behind a one-way mirror to record whether the child played with the forbidden toy or with a number of other less attractive toys that were available.

Regardless of the disincentive condition, very few children played with the forbidden toy. That's a critical point. The mild threat was sufficient to prevent the undesirable behavior. Then, the experimenter tested which condition produced the most self-persuasion by assessing the children's preference for the toys or providing them an opportunity to play with the forbidden toy later without the disincentive.

In a classic study by Jonathan Freedman (1965), for example, another experimenter returned to the school where forty-four boys had participated in a Mild or Severe Threat condition six weeks earlier. The experimenter took the boys out of class individually, and with no reference to the prior study, instructed each boy to take a drawing test. While scoring the test, the experimenter told the boy he could play with any toy in the room. The same five toys from the previous study were available, including the forbidden toy.

Of the boys from the Severe Threat condition, seventeen (77%) played with the forbidden toy, compared to only seven (32%) from the Mild Threat condition. Presumably, more children given the mild disincentive adopted a self-perception consistent with their avoidance of the attractive toy during the earlier session. Through self-persuasion, they developed a rationale for avoiding the previously forbidden toy in the absence of an external punishment contingency.

In an instructive follow-up experiment in 1971, Marc Lepper (as cited by Bem 1972) tempted young boys (with an appealing prize) to falsify their scores on a test he gave them. Three weeks earlier in another setting, these same subjects had resisted playing with the forbidden toy following a mild or severe threat. Those boys who had earlier received the mild threat were significantly less likely to cheat than those who had received the severe threat. Apparently, the boys who earlier complied with only a mild threat were more likely to develop a self-perception such as, "I'm a good boy who resists temptation."

Such internal dialogue or self-persuasion influenced resistance to temptation to cheat three weeks later.

Is there a message here for workplace programs designed to motivate compliance with safety regulations? Language like "compliance" and "regulation" clearly puts the control on the outside of people. Now add the threat of a fine or losing one's job. These kinds of contingencies will certainly motivate people to follow rules that are enforced, but don't expect such disincentives to encourage the kind of self-persuasion needed when people work alone with no one to hold them accountable except themselves. Thus, enforcement not only contributes to a negative attitude and stifles constructive conversation, as discussed in Chapter 1, it can prevent the kind of self-persuasion and ownership needed for long-term involvement in a safety process.

Obvious External Control Hinders Self-Persuasion

To decide how a particular situation might influence your own or another person's self-persuasion, try this. Imagine you're watching the individual (either yourself or another person) performing a particular behavior under a particular accountability system or set of circumstances. Then ask yourself this question: Are there sufficient external consequences to justify the amount of effort demonstrated? If your answer is "yes," then the performer is not likely to develop an internal justification for the behavior. If your answer is "no," then you could assume some internal dialogue or self-persuasion has occurred or is occurring.

Bottom line: It's necessary to promote self-persuasion and self-directed behavior whenever resources are insufficient to keep incentives or disincentives in place to sustain desired and effortful participation over the long term. This means the ABC principle (activator-behavior-consequence) of behavior-based safety must be strong enough to get the behavior started, but not sufficient to provide complete justification for the effort. This allows for self-persuasion and maintenance of participation when an external accountability system is no longer available.

Self-Persuasion and Hypocrisy

Which of the following conditions will produce the most participation for occupational safety?

- *Awareness*—Participants receive a clear and persuasive rationale about the need to wear safety glasses and hearing protection in a certain work area.

- *Awareness + Commitment*—Participants receive the convincing rationale and then publicly sign a pledge card, promising to wear this PPE under specified circumstances for one month.

- *Commitment + Hypocrisy*—Participants publicly sign a pledge card to wear safety glasses and ear plugs and then derive a list of situations in which they should wear this PPE but don't, like when mowing the grass in their back yard.

The first condition represents the typical educational approach to gaining compliance with certain industrial safety regulations. I'll bet basic intuition tells you the second condition will be more influential than the first. It causes more participation because of the consistency principle illustrated below. Simply put, when we make a choice or take a stand, we encounter personal and social pressures to perform consistently with our commitment.

Thus, you would expect more PPE use with the Awareness + Commitment intervention than with Awareness only. When people make a public statement to do something, they feel obligated to follow through. But behavioral research suggests that the third intervention—Commitment + Hypocrisy—

Prior commitment biases present decisions.

would be most influential in motivating PPE use. Why? Because of a special kind of self-persuasion. I'll explain what this means, but first let's review the empirical evidence.

Examining the Evidence. Elliot Aronson, one of the world's most honored social psychologists, and his students conducted a series of experiments to demonstrate the power of combining a commitment intervention with a procedure that reminded participants of their hypocrisy—inconsistencies between their commitment and their prior behavior. Their most cited research targeted AIDS prevention (Aronson, Fried, and Stone 1991).

Briefly, one group of sexually active college students increased their awareness of the AIDS problem by composing arguments for a speech about the value of using condoms to prevent AIDS. A "Commitment" group not only wrote the speech but also recorded it on a videotape that purportedly would be shown to high school students. Then half of the participants in each group listed circumstances in which they did not use condoms. Participants in a control group only received information about the use of condoms to prevent AIDS.

After exposure to one of these conditions, each student was privately given an opportunity to buy condoms at a special reduced price with the money they received for participating in the experiment. Those in the Hypocrisy group—the participants who made a list of their past behaviors that were inconsistent with their commitment to practice safe sex with condoms—were far more likely to buy condoms than those students in any of the other groups. Furthermore, several months later in a telephone interview, those students who had been made aware of their own hypocrisy reported significantly more use of condoms than students in the other groups.

Dr. Aronson and his colleagues replicated this hypocrisy effect in two additional studies—one targeting water conservation (Dickerson et al. 1992) and the other addressing resource recycling (Fried and Aronson 1995). Participants first made a public commitment to take a certain course of action, and then completed an exercise that reminded them of their failures to perform according to their commitment. In both studies, the hypocrisy exercise led to more desired behavior—shorter showers and more recycling—than the awareness or commitment approaches.

Explaining the Effect. How can the hypocrisy effect be explained? Why does this kind of intervention influence more behavior change than standard awareness and commitment procedures? If you visualize yourself in the various conditions of the experiments outlined above, you'll understand the influential power of hypocrisy.

Let's return to the consistency principle. Given people's desire to keep their words in line with their actions and vice versa, having them remind themselves of an inconsistency between what they say they will do and what they actually do leads to internal conflict or tension. Social psychologists call this "cognitive dissonance" (Festinger 1957). You could say the inconsistency causes a certain kind of internal dialogue or self-persuasion.

This internal tension is not a pleasant state. It challenges one's personal honesty. How do you reduce this tension and restore a sense of integrity? Easy—simply change your behavior to make it consistent with your commitment. The important point here is that evoking this tension by inciting people to perceive an inconsistency between personal commitment and action led to more desired participation than a standard awareness or commitment exercise. Does this inspire any ideas for increasing the impact of your next attempt to persuade others to perform certain safety-related behaviors?

Applying the Hypocrisy Effect to Safety. I could find no safety applications of this hypocrisy intervention. But I'm sure you can think of various ways to use this technique to increase participation in safety-improvement efforts. As outlined in Figure 4.1, simply ask people to commit publicly to do something for safety, and then ask them to think of times when their behavior has been inconsistent with their commitment. Your objective is to stir up feelings of being hypocritical or inconsistent.

Of course, you need to obtain the initial commitment, and that could be a challenge in some situations. However, I've found it easy to get people to state openly that they hold safety as a "core value." It's common for workers

Figure 4.1 The four steps to increasing safety participation with the hypocrisy effect. The first two steps are other-directed (from the trainer or facilitator), while the latter two steps are self-directed (initiated by the recipient of the intervention).

OTHER-DIRECTED

- *Obtain a public commitment that safety is a core value.*

- *Ask for a list of actions that are inconsistent with holding safety as a value.*

SELF-DIRECTED

- *Create tension between words and deeds.*

- *Reduce conflict and restore a sense of integrity by changing actions to align with the commitment.*

to admit that the greatest reward for supporting a safety initiative is to go home in one piece and to see their coworkers do the same.

Safety must be a core value, not just a priority. Try facilitating a discussion that leads to participants publicly voicing their commitment to safety as a core value. This might be enough to establish a context for the hypocrisy effect. Next, ask employees who claim safety as a value to make a list of things they do in their work areas that are inconsistent with holding safety as a value. Should the list be private or public? That's a question in need of systematic research.

Testing Ideas. Since no safety research has evaluated the hypocrisy effect, I cannot offer more details about how to apply this promising technique for increasing participation in occupational safety. The following empirical questions, for example, need answers:

- Should the list of inconsistencies be private or public?

- Suppose it's possible to create *group* tension by obtaining group consensus that safety is a value, and then listing specific behaviors observed by group members that are inconsistent with safety as a value. Would this exercise lead to a group hypocrisy effect?

- Can group hypocrisy be developed when team members are motivated to reduce collective tension by adjusting their personal and interpersonal behaviors?

- Would a group approach be more efficient and effective at increasing safety-related participation than the individual approach used in the research literature?

- How long will the beneficial behavioral impact of the hypocrisy effect last?

These are only a few of many questions about the hypocrisy effect that deserve systematic study. So what's holding you back? Test the hypocrisy effect in various situations, and please let me know what you find out. We have much more to learn about ways to increase prevention participation in occupational safety.

Self-Persuasion and Mindfulness

The topic of self-persuasion relates directly to the critical distinction between mindful and mindless behavior (Langer 1989, 1997). Have you ever found yourself somewhere with no recollection of how you got there? You know it took several decisions and behaviors to get there, but you don't remember processing information and completing the sequence of tasks. This even happens to people while driving a vehicle. They arrive at a particular destination, perhaps even the wrong place, but they are not mindful of the series of choices they made to get there. It's as if the vehicle "drove itself," an expression we use to acknowledge the results of a routine set of behaviors. In this example, behavior has become mindless.

People sometimes move through daily regimes with little thought, alertness, or creativity. The more mundane and commonplace the activity, the more likely a person will use an unconscious script to guide behavior and fall into a state of unawareness. This is mindless activity, and social psychologists warn us that in this state we are particularly susceptible to slick marketing and social influence tactics such as sales pitches and authoritative directives. The salesperson illustrated below, for example, is relying on mindlessness to impress potential customers.

How many injuries occur because people were "just not thinking"? How often do we get into a set work routine involving a sequence of behaviors that we perform unconsciously? We take our mind off the process and put

Some sales pitches count on mindlessness.

ourselves on automatic pilot. This is fine if all the habitual behaviors are safe, but what if a risky shortcut is interspersed in the behavioral sequence? What if an environmental event requires us to quickly adjust our behavior? Will our mindlessness prevent prompt reaction? Without even realizing it, our mindless work practice puts us at risk for injury.

The Limits of Habit

The term "habit" is used often in the context of behavior-based safety. It essentially means we get into a regular routine of doing something so fluently it's done without thinking. In other words, a habit is a behavior that occurs automatically, without conscious thought. I've heard many behavior-based safety trainers claim this to be the optimal state for desired behavior. More specifically, some behavior-based safety specialists advocate the use of intervention techniques to increase the fluency of behavior until it reaches a habitual state.

But habitual means mindless, and therefore, as discussed above, habitual behaviors are not ideal. I'm convinced the ultimate objective of behavior-based interventions should be "mindful fluency." However, this calls for a consideration of mental scripting, which is similar to self-persuasion.

When we are mindful about our proficient actions, we talk to ourselves about the desirable behaviors we perform. Before executing a behavior, we might give ourselves a mental reminder that the particular situation calls for a certain response. Being mindful while performing a behavior means we are describing our actions to ourselves as we work. And after a behavior occurs, the mindful actor ponders an evaluation or interpretation. This is "mental scripting" as it should occur before, during, and after ongoing behavior. Here are five reasons for recommending mindful fluency over habitual (presumably mindless) behavior.

Mindfulness Prevents Human Error. Perhaps the most obvious benefit of mindful behavior is that it prevents performing in the automatic mode, as discussed above. How many times a day do you take your mind off the process and put yourself on automatic pilot? This can obviously lead to a serious error or an injury. By avoiding the automatic mode, we prevent those errors and injuries that occur because we were "just not thinking."

Mindfulness Allows for Stimulus Discrimination. Habitual routines work when the environment or context in which we are performing remains constant. But what if an unexpected environmental stimulus, such as a fork-lift truck speeding around a corner, requires us to immediately adjust our behavior? We need to be able to discriminate quickly between the normal routine and the suddenly different work context. We need to be flexible and draw on new information rather than rely on the past. Also, if we're not mindful, we can habituate to an incremental degradation of our work context and not recognize a need to discriminate and adjust our behavior or fix the environment. This is less likely when we become more mindful of our everyday activities.

Mindfulness Facilitates Generalization. Generalization comes in two forms—*stimulus generalization* and *response generalization* (Ludwig and Geller 2001). Just as mindless habitual behavior prevents stimulus discrimination, it can also deter stimulus generalization or the appropriate transfer of behavior from one setting to another. For example, the use of ear and eye protection in the workplace should generalize to relevant situations at home, such as mowing the lawn in one's back yard.

Response generalization occurs when the occurrence of one behavior influences the performance of another similar behavior in the same context. This happens, for example, when using a vehicle safety belt reminds a driver to also use turn signals and travel at safe speeds.

Interventions that influence participants to say to themselves "I'm doing this because I have to" are unlikely to promote much useful generalization. But when an intervention enables personal choice, self-direction, and perceptions of empowerment (as discussed in Chapter 2), the mindful script is more like, "We are doing this because we choose to in order to benefit everyone." This is the kind of mindfulness that results in beneficial stimulus and response generalization.

Mindfulness Enhances Safety Responsibility. Many claim they buckle up in their vehicles automatically, without even thinking about it. Such mindless behavior is commendable, but is not ideal. When you habitually buckle up without self-talk, you lose an opportunity to reward yourself for going out of your way to be safe. Plus, in this automatic state you might not notice that a passenger in your vehicle is not using a safety belt.

On the other hand, mindful awareness of your own safety-belt use, accompanied by complementary self-talk, increases the probability of noticing whether others are also buckled up for safety. If your mental script supports the self-concept of "responsible safety leader," you will likely actively care for an unbuckled vehicle occupant.

Mindfulness Increases Actively Caring. When you actively care for the safety and health of others, give yourself mental credit for such action and become mindful of your good deed. Just like extrinsic positive reinforcement, self-reinforcement increases the frequency of the behavior it follows. Self-management studies have shown that people who reward themselves are more likely to remain self-accountable and improve their performance (Watson and Tharp 1997). This is most likely to occur when the mindful self-talk leads to an actual extrinsic reward. In this case, the mindfulness following a safe behavior includes a decision to give oneself an opportunity to do something enjoyable after doing something less fun but important for safety and health.

Becoming More Mindful

It is to our advantage to become less mindless and more mindful of behavioral routines that could lead to injury, either to ourselves or to others. How can we do this? First, we can attempt to focus on the various process activities of our job. Write down the distinct steps of a task, and reflect on the possibilities of an at-risk behavior and injury at each step. Perhaps this has already been done in the job safety analysis (JSA) of your job, but that JSA could be long forgotten. A lot may have happened since, and maybe you weren't even involved in conducting the analysis.

Optimal mindfulness of complex activities is not something you achieve on your own. It requires the support of others. A good example of group consciousness-raising is the development of a critical behavior checklist (CBC). Everyone in the group participates. This has several benefits:

- People become mindful of the safe steps of a certain job.

- Mindfulness is spread across several individuals at once.

- People become more aware that maximum mindfulness and protection from injury occur when people look out for each other.

Let's consider the mindfulness that results from using a CBC. Behavior-based trainers and consultants often focus on the power of behavioral feedback in increasing safe behaviors and reducing workplace injuries. In fact, I've heard some behavioral consultants proclaim that feedback is the most important behavior-change feature of an observation and feedback process. I'll cover various feedback procedures in the next two chapters. Here I'd like you to realize another benefit of an observation and feedback process.

As indicated above, mindfulness about specific safety-related behaviors is increased significantly when a work team develops a CBC. But even more mindfulness occurs when a CBC is actually used. This mindfulness is most immediately relevant for injury prevention.

Imagine one coworker approaching another who's hard at work and asking, "Is this a good time for a behavioral audit?" Whether the answer is "yes" or "no," some amount of safety mindfulness is raised. Now think about the impact of the actual observation process. After volunteering to be observed, the worker is now mindful of every aspect of his or her work process. The employee not only thinks about the specific items on the checklist, but tries to be cognizant of every possible safety-related behavior of the task.

In the right context, the observed employee actually shows off individual ability to work safely. This is mindfulness at its best. It is initiated by an observation process that includes several key elements: communication is open and direct, the focus is on behaviors, and the observation is conducted with permission. This helps to build the proper context—an atmosphere of inter-personal trust and mutual actively caring—helping each other for the safety of all. It's not blind trust, as illustrated below, but is developed through mindful one-on-one conversation.

The individual feedback portion of this behavioral coaching process is certainly important. It serves to support the safe decisions a coworker makes, and provides an opportunity to improve the safety of a job. This kind of feedback also makes both employees, the person observed and the observer, more mindful of the many environmental and behavioral facets of the work process that could cause personal injury. I'm convinced this increased mindfulness is one of the most influential outcomes of a behavior-based observation and feedback process, contributing significantly to its remarkable injury-prevention success.

Blind trust can be hazardous.

In Conclusion

This chapter discussed participation within a mental or thinking framework. While the aim is to increase safety-related behavior, the principles and procedures presented here took us beyond behavior-based safety. Specifically, self-persuasion is not objectively observable as behavior, but this mental activity plays a critical role in sustaining long-term participation or behavior change. Moreover, the situations most likely to facilitate self-persuasion are not all consistent with the standard behavior-based perspective.

Social and cognitive psychologists have shown self-persuasion to be facilitated most often when direct outside control is not obvious. This is consistent with the theme of Chapter 1—that the kind of long-term and comprehensive participation needed to sustain an injury-free workplace cannot be dictated. Although positive reinforcement procedures feel less controlling than the enforcement approach, behavior-based rewards can also hinder the development of self-persuasion, depending on their size and the method of delivery.

The next chapter explains the best ways to administer a reward and recognition program to enhance involvement in occupational safety. For now, realize this bottom line: The more obvious an external accountability system, the greater the disconnection between behavior and self-perception, and the less self-persuasion and sustained participation when the intervention is removed.

Safety participation can be increased and injuries decreased by a mental process similar to self-participation—mindfulness. It's easy to fall into a mindless job routine and become incapable of handling unexpected events in a safe and timely manner. Plus, some mindless behavior can put a person at immediate risk for personal injury. We need to understand that this can happen to anyone and warrants a concerted effort to increase people's mindfulness on the job.

A behavior-based observation and feedback process provides the mechanism for making this happen. But to get the best from such a process we need to be mindful of what it takes to develop and maintain an atmosphere of interpersonal trust and actively caring participation. Improving the quality and increasing the quantity of safety communication is essential, as explained in the next chapter. Later, in Chapter 8, I describe the essentials of interpersonal trust, including how to spread it throughout a work culture.

5

The Support of Safety Conversation

*Interpersonal conversation defines the culture in which we work. It
can create conflict and build barriers to safety improvement. Or, it
can cultivate the kind of work culture needed to make a major break-
through in injury prevention. Interpersonal conversation also affects
our intrapersonal conversations or self-talk, which in turn influences
our willingness to get involved in safety-improvement efforts. This
chapter explains the reciprocal impact of inter- and intrapersonal conversation, and offers guidelines for aligning both toward nurturing the
kind of continuous participation needed to achieve and maintain an
injury-free workplace.*

You've heard the expression "Talk is cheap." Now consider the remarkable influence of "talking" on our feelings, attitudes, perceptions,
knowledge, skills, and behavior. You cannot deny the fact that talking is the
most cost-effective intervention we have to improve the human dynamics of
any situation.

Every topic in this book relates directly to the theme of this chapter. In
Chapter 1 we started our conversation about participation for occupational safety
with a focus on how enforcement approaches to safety stifle the kind of constructive communication needed to analyze negative incidents—from near hits
and at-risk behavior to serious injuries—and reduce their future occurrence.

The new E-word for occupational safety—empowerment—was discussed
in Chapter 2. The ingredients of true empowerment were defined, and various
methods for increasing feelings of empowerment were presented. The foundation of all these techniques was conversation, whether in group training
sessions, during one-to-one behavioral coaching, or when talking to oneself.
Deciding to participate or to not get involved boils down to personal deci-

sion making, or intrapersonal conversation. Factors influencing our decisions to participate on behalf of someone else were entertained in Chapter 3.

In Chapter 4, the focus was on a special kind of conversation—self-persuasion. Here I reviewed the need for certain kinds of self-talk to sustain participation in the absence of an external accountability system. Research-based methods for increasing this type of intrapersonal conversation were introduced and contrasted with approaches that do not benefit self-persuasion.

This chapter continues our discussion (actually a conversation) about the power of conversation to increase the quantity and improve the quality of participation in occupational safety. In a sense, we're back to the basics here—examining how we can talk more effectively to others and to ourselves about occupational safety. The result will be more fuel for *The Participation Factor*. Yes, talk is cheap, but it can make or break your efforts to make a difference.

The Potency of Conversation

At the start of this book, I stated my conviction that participation in actively caring conversations about how to improve safety is key to achieving an injury-free workplace. I'm not talking about high-tech communication, but one-to-one conversation about safety. Such improvement, in turn, benefits people's self-talk or intrapersonal communication about safety, increasing one's sense of empowerment to prevent occupational injuries.

This chapter offers guidelines and techniques for getting more beneficial impact from our communications with others and with ourselves. Then four types of safety management are presented, each defined by the nature of inter-personal conversation. However, I can't expect you to spend the time and effort needed to improve communications until you truly appreciate the power of conversation. So let's consider the impact of effective conversation.

Building Interpersonal Barriers

Almost everyone has seen how lack of communication can escalate a minor incident into a major conflict. Here's an example: You see a coworker and say, "Hello," yet she passes by without reacting. Maybe she didn't see you or had other thoughts on her mind. Still, it's easy for you to assume she is unfriendly or doesn't like you. So the next time you see her, you avoid being friendly. You might even talk about her "unfriendliness" to others. I think you can see how a barrier starts to build.

This is only one of many situations that can stifle interpersonal communication and lead to negative feelings and judgments. The possible result: the perception of interpersonal conflict, an unpleasant relationship, lowered work output, or reduced willingness to participate for another person's safety.

Resolving Interpersonal Conflict

If the lack of conversation can initiate or energize conflict, it's not surprising that the occurrence of conversation can prevent or eliminate conflict. "Let's talk it out," as the saying goes. Of course, it's the quality of that conversation that will determine whether any perceived conflict is heightened or lessened. This issue of conversation quality is covered later in this chapter. Here I only want you to consider the potency of interpersonal talk. It can make or break interpersonal conflict, which in turn enables destructive or constructive relationships. And the nature of relationships determines whether individuals are willing to actively care for another person's safety and health (Geller 1994, 2001a).

Making Intangibles Real

What are love, friendship, courage, loyalty, happiness, and forgiveness? Yes, you can describe behaviors that reflect these concepts, but where is the true meaning? Don't we derive the meaning of these common words from our conversations? Consider how we "fall in or out of love" depending on how we talk to ourselves and others. Similarly, we convince ourselves we're happy through our self-talk, and this inner conversation is obviously influenced by what we hear others say about us.

We define another person's friendship, courage, or loyalty by talking about that individual in certain ways, both to ourselves and to others. Our mental scripts and verbal behavior are powerful. They give meaning to concepts that define the very essence of human existence. And when groups, organizations, or communities communicate to explain these concepts, we call it a "culture." Indeed, our culture is defined by conversations—both spoken and unspoken —and the behaviors influenced by such communication.

Defining Culture

What about "unspoken conversation"? I'm referring to customs or unwritten rules we heed without mention. We might realize, for example, the "teacher's pets" sit in the front row, or the boss doesn't want to hear about a "near miss," or the real purpose of the safety incentive program is to stifle the reporting of OSHA recordables. We might also know factors that bias certain managers' performance appraisals, from gender and seniority to ability on the golf course.

It might be understood that a male with high seniority and a low golf handicap is more likely to get the special training assignment, but such prejudice is certainly not expressed. If it were, a productive conversation would be possible—one that could reduce the conflict and bias that hinder maximum participation in optimizing a work system and achieving an injury-free workplace.

The bottom line: Spoken and unspoken words define cultures and subcultures, and then cultures can change, for better or worse, through interpersonal and intrapersonal conversation.

Influencing Self-Esteem

How we talk to ourselves both influences and reflects our self-esteem. In fact, it's probably fair to say our mental script about ourselves *is* our self-esteem. We can focus our self-talk on the good or bad things people say about us. The result is a certain kind of self-talk we call "interpretation." Our self-esteem can go up or down according to how we talk to ourselves about the way others talk about us.

Self-talk can influence our behavior, and in turn affect our self-efficacy, personal control, and optimism. The illustration below reflects a true story. My daughter, a scholarship athlete on the University of West Florida basketball team, stole the ball under the opponent's basket and drove the length of the court to

Negative self-talk can help you miss the mark.

attempt a critical tie-breaking basket. She missed, however, because she put herself in a failure mindset. She didn't *tell* herself she expected to miss, but just the suggestion of missing the critical shot might have set her up for failure.

I'll bet no reader is surprised or impressed by this story. You've probably been in similar situations many times. It's just one more demonstration of a self-fulfilling prophecy. Note, however, that the intrapersonal conversation does not need to state the expectation of failure. Just suggesting a negative rather than a positive outcome can be enough to limit success.

I should add that my conversations with my daughter about her negative self-talk persuaded her to discuss this issue with all of her teammates as well as various members of the university softball team. She told me her focus on positive, achievement-oriented self-talk during games has improved her performance. In addition, she's convinced the factor most responsible for dramatically improving her best friend's batting average was stopping the negative self-talk that had routinely occurred whenever she stepped up to the plate.

Negative self-talk puts your mind and body in failure mode.

The Challenge of Improving Conversation

Given the power of conversation to resolve interpersonal conflict, define culture, and affect self-esteem and feelings of empowerment, we need to direct this powerful tool to support involvement in occupational safety. But how do we maximize the impact of our interpersonal and intrapersonal conversations? What kinds of conversations are more likely to encourage and maintain beneficial participation in occupational safety? That's the theme for the remainder of this chapter. Let's start with the most basic aspect of communication—the words we use to talk about safety.

Watch Your Language

Words shape our feelings, expectancies, attitudes, and behavior (Hayakawa 1978). How you talk about something influences how you and others feel about it. In other words, your current verbal behavior affects your attitudes and beliefs, and these in turn influence your subsequent behavior. Question: Does your safety-related language increase or decrease employee involvement in safety-related activities?

I think some words we use in the safety and health fields are counterproductive. They are negative and uninspiring, and probably have a detrimental effect on *The Participation Factor*. Let me point out a few that should be eliminated from our safety vocabulary.

Say "Injury"—Not "Accident." The word "accident" implies a chance occurrence outside your immediate control. When a young child has an "accident" in his pants, we presume he was not in control. He couldn't help it.

Workplace "accidents" are usually unintentional, of course, but are they truly chance occurrences? There are usually specific controllable factors, such as the environment, behaviors, and/or attitudes, that can prevent "accidents."

Do you remember when our president Bill Clinton stumbled on the steps at the home of golf pro Greg Norman in West Palm Beach, Florida? It happened on the morning of March 14, 1997. When asked about the incident, Clinton was quoted in our local newspaper (*The Roanoke Times*) as saying, "It was just an accident. Accidents happen to people." The logical follow-up comment is, "When it's your time, it's your time." How many times have you heard someone say something like that?

Clinton's remark reflects the meaning of "accident." "Accidents are bound to happen somewhere to someone. It's only a matter of time before it happens here. I just hope my luck doesn't run out and it happens to me." These statements are not far-fetched. They follow logically from the meaning of "accident."

Incidentally, do you recall any reports of an "accident investigation" of Clinton's injury? We heard much about the extent of his injury—a tear of his quadriceps tendon, which connects the upper thigh to the kneecap. And we were told about his knee surgery at Bethesda Naval Hospital. We even got a play-by-play on his recovery, as he progressed over several weeks from a big brace and crutches to a cane. But nothing was mentioned about the factors contributing to the incident. What was the "root cause"?

Were the steps slippery? Did someone distract the president? Did the president fail to use the handrail, or was a handrail unavailable? Did someone "accidentally" push Mr. Clinton? Where were the bodyguards? Could a bodyguard have warned the president about an environmental hazard or offered feedback about his at-risk behavior? The answers to these questions and others could provide an incident analysis that would help prevent future mishaps to the president and to others in similar circumstances.

Imagine the nationwide impact if a careful analysis of the potential contributing causes of Clinton's injury had been conducted and reported. Consider the benefits of broad media coverage of the potential environment-, behavior-, and person-based factors that led to the president's injury and the techniques that could be implemented to prevent future mishaps like this one. Bodyguards might even add safe versus at-risk behaviors of the president and his companions to the regular protective audits they perform. However, none of this participation in injury prevention is likely to occur with the attitude that "It was just an accident, and accidents happen to people."

We want to develop the belief and expectation in our work culture that injuries can be prevented by controlling certain factors. Therefore, "accident" is the wrong word to use when referring to an unintentional injury. Using this word can reduce the number of people who believe with true conviction that their participation in safety efforts can prevent personal injuries. Besides, if the incident caused an injury, then the word "injury" has more impact than "accident." For the same reason, it's not a vehicle "accident"; it's a vehicle "crash."

Say "Incident Analysis"—Not "Investigation." What about the word "investigation," as in "accident investigation" or "criminal investigation." Doesn't this word imply a hunt for some one thing or person to blame for a particular incident? How can we promote fact-finding over fault-finding with a term like "investigation" defining our job assignment?

To learn more about how to prevent injuries from an analysis of an incident, we need to approach the task with a different mindset. It's not "accident investigation." It's "incident analysis." This simple change in our language can lead to more participation in this critical process for preventing injuries. But please don't look for one "root cause."

A common myth in the safety field is that injuries are caused by one critical factor—the root cause. "Ask enough questions," advises the safety consultant, "and you'll arrive at the critical factor behind an injury." I've actually heard it said that if you ask "Why?" five times you'll arrive at the root cause. Come on—do you really believe there's a single root cause of an incident, whether it's a near hit, damage to property, or personal injury?

Recall the three sides of the safety culture triad discussed in Chapter 1 (see Figure 1.1 on page 3) as a framework for defining the challenges of injury prevention. One side is for environment-based factors, including tools, equipment, engineering design, climate, and housekeeping. Another side is behavior factors: the actions everyone did or did not perform related to an incident. And the third side represents person factors—the internal feeling states of the people involved in the incident, including their attitudes, perceptions, and personality characteristics.

Given the dynamic interdependency of these three factors in everyday events, how can anyone expect to find one root cause of an incident? Instead, take a systems approach and search for a variety of contributory factors within the three domains. Then decide which of these factors can be changed to reduce the chance of another unfortunate incident. Environment factors are usually easiest to define and improve, followed by behavior factors. Most difficult to define and change directly are the person factors, but many of these can be improved indirectly with proper delivery of a behavior-improvement process (Daniels 2000; Geller 1998b, 2001d; McSween 1995).

Say "Safety Belt"—Not "Restraint." For more than two decades I've been urging transportation and safety professionals to stop using the terms "occupant restraints" and "child restraints" for vehicle safety belts and child safety seats. These terms imply discomfort and lack of personal control. Furthermore, these labels fail to convey the true function of these devices. "Seat belt" is better than "occupant restraint," but this popular term is not really adequate because it doesn't describe the function or appearance of today's lap-and-shoulder belts. We need to get into the habit of saying "safety belt" and "child safety seat." Actually, "life belt" and "life-saving seat" are even more appropriate terms.

Say "Value"—Not "Priority." Priority implies importance and a sense of urgency, and safety professionals are often quick to say, "Safety should be a priority." This seems appropriate, since my *New Merriam-Webster Dictionary* defines "priority" as "taking precedence logically or in importance" (p. 577). But everyday experience teaches us that priorities come and go. Depending upon the demands of the moment, one priority often gets swapped for another. Do we really want to put safety on such shifting ground?

I believe an injury-free workplace requires safety to be accepted as a "value." The relevant definition of "value" in my dictionary is "something (as a principle or ideal) intrinsically valuable or desirable" (p. 800). Safety

*Some words
inhibit
participation.*

should be a "value" that employees bring to every job, regardless of the on-going priorities or task requirements. When safety is communicated as a value, the Hypocrisy Effect can be used to enhance participation, as I discussed in Chapter 4.

Say "Behavior Analysis"—Not "Behavior Modification." In recent years I've seen "behavior modification" used many times in titles of safety presentations at regional and national conferences. I've heard trainers, consultants, and employees use the term to describe behavior-based safety. In fact, I've often been introduced at conferences as a specialist in "behavior modification." This is the wrong choice of words to use if we want acceptance and involvement from the folks who are to be "modified." Who wants to be "modified"?

This lesson was learned the hard way more than thirty years ago by the behavioral scientists and therapists who developed the principles and techniques of "behavior modification." Whether it applied to teachers, students, employees, or prisoners, the term "behavior modification" was a real turn-off. It conveyed images of manipulation, top-down control, loss of personal control, and "Big Brother."

Unfortunately, the term "behavior" alone carries negative associations for many—as in "Let's talk about your behavior last night"—but I can't see any way around using it. Behavior refers to process—the ongoing work practices that result in certain output or outcomes. We need to teach and demonstrate the benefits of focusing on behaviors and on defining behaviors correctly.

As I detail elsewhere (Geller 2001c), the words used to describe behavior should be chosen for *clarity* to avoid being misinterpreted, for *precision* to fit a specific activity, for *brevity* to keep it simple, and for *objectivity* to refer to actions explicitly observed. Without a clear and precise definition of behavior, most action words can have more than one interpretation.

If you want to encourage participation in behavior-based safety, don't link the word "modification" with behavior. "Behavior analysis" is the term used by researchers and scholars in this area of applied psychology. This implies that behavior is analyzed first, and if change is called for, an intervention process is developed with input from the clients. Thus, we have a behavior-based analysis, then a behavior-based intervention leading to behavior-based improvement. This contrasts nicely with the "person-based" approach that focuses on analyzing and changing attitudes, feelings, and expectancies. As I emphasized in Chapter 4, maximizing *The Participation Factor* requires consideration of both behavior-based and person-based psychology.

I hope the basic message is clear. We need to understand that our language can activate feelings and even behaviors we don't want. It can hinder participation. If we want to communicate in order to "sell" a safety process, we must consider how our language will be perceived by those whose participation is needed to make the process work.

Ponder the following words and phrases related to occupational safety. Do some of the words or phrases on the left suggest negative associations that can harm *The Participation Factor?* I suggest alternatives on the right, but you may have better ideas.

"Air bag"	or "safety cushion"?
"Peer pressure"	or "peer support"?
"Program"	or "process"?
"Training"	or "coaching"?
"Loss control manger"	or "safety facilitator"?
"Compliance"	or "accomplishment"?
"Meeting OSHA standards"	or "fulfilling a corporate mission"?
"Thirty days without an injury"	or "thirty safe days"?
"I've got to do this"	or "I get to do this."
"I must meet this deadline"	or "I choose to achieve another milestone"?

Considering the ramifications of using these terms and phrases is a good personal or group exercise. Adding alternatives to this list is even more beneficial. But understanding the critical relationship between words, attitudes, and participation is only half the battle. We need to change verbal habits, and this is easier said than done. Also, the effectiveness of our communication to facilitate participation depends on more than the words we use. Let's turn to other aspects of our interpersonal conversations that affect impact.

Don't Look Back

Has this ever happened to you? You ask for more safety involvement from a particular individual and you get a reaction like this: "I served on a safety team three years ago and we got nothing done, so count me out." Or, have you attended a safety meeting where people spend more time going over past accomplishments or failures than discussing future possibilities and deriving action plans?

These are examples of conversations stuck in the past. Conversations about past events help us connect with others and recognize similar experiences, opinions, and motives. However, such communication does not permit progress toward problem solving or continuous improvement. For this to happen, the conversation must leave the past and move on.

Kim Krisco (1997) maintains that leaders need to help people move their conversations from the past to the future and then back to the present. If you want conversation to fuel *The Participation Factor,* possibilities need to be entertained (future talk) and then practical action plans need to be developed (present talk). This is the case for group conversation at a team meeting as well as for one-on-one advising, counseling, or safety coaching.

To direct the flow of a conversation from past to future and then to the present, you first must recognize and appreciate what the other person has to say. Then shift the focus toward the future. Remember, you're approaching this person to discuss possibilities for safety improvement and specific ways to get started now.

Seek Commitment

You know your interpersonal conversation is especially productive when someone makes a commitment to participate. This reflects success in moving conversation from the past to the future and then to a specific action plan. As discussed in Chapter 4, a verbal commitment also tells you something is happening on an intrapersonal level—as in self-persuasion. The person is becoming self-motivated, increasing the probability participation will continue in the absence of an external accountability system (Cialdini 2001).

Now you can proceed to talk about how the commitment can be supported or how to hold the individual accountable. For example, one person might offer to help a coworker meet an obligation through verbal reminders. Or an individual might agree to honor a commitment by showing a coach behavioral records that verify participation. This is the kind of follow-up conversation that facilitates continued involvement.

Stop and Listen

In their eagerness to prevent injury, safety advocates sometimes give corrective feedback in a top-down, controlling manner. In other words, passion for safety can lead to an overly directive approach to get others to change their behavior. As I discussed in Chapter 4, an indirect or nondirective approach to giving advice is usually more effective, especially over the long term (Bandura 1997; Ryan and Deci 2000).

Think about it: How do you respond when someone tells you specifically what to do? Now it certainly depends on who is giving the instruction, but I'll bet your reaction is not entirely positive. You might follow the instruction, especially if it comes from someone with the power to control consequences. But how will you feel? Will you be motivated to make a permanent change? You might if you asked for the direction. But if you didn't request feedback, you could feel insulted or embarrassed. Try to be more nondirective when using interpersonal conversation to affect behavior change. As Stephen Covey (1989) recommends with his fifth habit for highly effective people, "Seek first to understand, then to be understood."

Ask Questions First

Instead of telling people what to do, try this: Get them to tell you, in their own words, what they ought to be doing in order to be safe. You can do this by asking questions with a sincere and caring attitude. At all costs avoid a sarcastic or demeaning tone. First, point out some safe behaviors you've noticed—it's important to emphasize positives. But don't give a general positive statement followed by specific negatives, as illustrated on the next page.

Then move on to the seemingly at-risk behavior by asking, "Is there a safer way to perform that task?" Of course, you hope for more than a "yes" or "no" response to a question like this. But if that's all you get, you need to be more precise in follow-up questioning. You might, for example, point out a particular work routine that seems risky, and ask whether there is a safer way.

I recommend approaching a corrective feedback conversation as if you don't know the safest procedures, even if you think you do. You might, in fact, find your presumptions to be imperfect. The "expert" on the job might know something you don't know.

By asking questions, you're always going to learn something. If nothing else, you'll hear the rationale behind taking a risk over choosing the safer alternative. You might uncover a barrier to safety that you can help the person overcome. A conversation that entertains ways to remove obstacles that hinder safe behavior is especially valuable if it translates possibilities into feasible and relevant action plans.

94

Behavior-based coaching should include more specifics about safe behavior than at-risk behavior.

Transition from Nondirective to Directive Conversation

What if the person doesn't give a satisfactory answer to your question about safer alternatives? What if he or she doesn't seem to know the safest operating procedure? Now you must shift from nondirective to directive conversation. You need to give behavior-focused advice. You certainly cannot react like the observer in the illustration on the next page and ignore at-risk behavior.

Open the conversation with a phrase that implies the person really does know the safe way to perform, but for some reason just overlooked (or forgot) it this time. This could happen to anyone. John Drebinger (1997) recommends starting with the phrase, "As you know." Such an opening can help prevent the individual from feeling his or her intelligence or safety knowledge has been insulted.

At-risk behavior cannot be ignored.

An Illustrative Anecdote

A conversation I had with a friend about a year ago demonstrates the power of interpersonal conversation. It reviews some important points about giving corrective feedback in such a way that it's accepted. In this case it might have saved a life.

One Sunday evening last May I received a very rewarding phone call from a long-time friend and colleague—Mike Hedlesky. For almost two years Mike has been managing the construction of my log lodge, so we have had frequent phone conversations. But this phone call was different. Before giving me a progress report on the lodge, Mike thanked me for possibly saving his life. Then he told me about his freak bicycle crash earlier that day.

He was traveling about twenty-five miles per hour when the rear wheel broke away from the frame. Mike sailed over the handlebars and hit the road head first. It happened so fast that he didn't even have time to put his hands up to break his fall. Mike's face was painfully bruised, but imagine how serious his injuries might have been if he had not been wearing a bike helmet. Mike claimed that he put the helmet on that day because of me—thus the reason for the "thank you."

Two weeks earlier I had seen Mike biking on a country road without a helmet. He was wearing a cowboy hat instead. There were no other vehicles on the road, so I drove my car beside him to say hello and we stopped for a brief conversation. After exchanging friendly words, I said I was surprised to see that he was not wearing a helmet. Then I reminded him of a bicycle crash I had experienced two years earlier in which my bike helmet probably saved my life. I also remarked that his girlfriend (now his wife) who was riding about fifty yards behind him, *was* wearing a helmet.

Mike told me he thought about that conversation when he and his girlfriend embarked on a bike ride the Sunday of his crash. As a result, he wore a helmet that day. And that protective behavior may well have saved his life. Five aspects of my conversation with Mike gave it the power to make a difference. They exemplify principles discussed in this chapter for benefiting *The Participation Factor*.

Show You Care

I did not criticize Mike for not using a bike helmet. Our conversation was friendly and not confrontational. Within the context of our friendship and my caring demeanor, my remarks about safety were accepted. I didn't admonish Mike for not being safe, nor did I tell him to comply with a safety rule. Instead, I only indicated surprise that he was not practicing a particular safe act. This approach created conflict or dissonance between his personal values and his overt behavior.

Expect the Best

When I noted a discrepancy between what I expected from Mike and his actual behavior, I may have created conflict or dissonance in him between his internal values and external behavior (recall the discussion of "cognitive dissonance," commitment, and self-persuasion in Chapter 4). In other words, I suggested that Mike was not the kind of person who would ride a bicycle without using the proper protective equipment. If Mike recognized an inconsistency between his safety values and his behavior in this situation, he felt some internal pressure to resolve the discrepancy. Perhaps this inconsistency was made more salient when I pointed out that his girlfriend was wearing a helmet.

Point Out Peer Practices

Reminding Mike that his biking partner was wearing a protective helmet probably did more than make him aware of the inconsistency between his personal values and behavior. It drove home the fact that the safe behavior in question was being practiced by others, including a significant other. And when his partner put on her bike helmet that critical Sunday, Mike followed her example, resolving any inconsistency he might have noted.

When safe behavior is viewed as the norm, we have social conformity on our side—a social influence principle I cover in more detail in Chapter 7. However, when desired behavior is not practiced by the majority, as is the case with bike-helmet use, it can be particularly useful to point out specific occurrences of the safe practice. As indicated in Chapter 1, a single case study is often persuasive, because it provides a clear example to follow. It also allows a supportive mental image to be formed that can be both directional and motivational.

Use Personal Testimony

In that critical conversation, I reminded Mike of my bicycle crash and how a bike helmet might have saved my life. I had told him the gory details two years earlier, soon after the crash. Perhaps my brief mentioning of that earlier incident provided Mike with an image that influenced his ultimate decision to use a bike helmet.

Why is personal testimony so influential? Well, it's personal and it's real. Listeners can visualize themselves in a similar situation and form a mental image of how they'd react to it. Later they can retrieve that image for personal direction and motivation. The image can be a negative one—something to avoid by wearing particular PPE or following certain operating procedures. Or it can be positive: they can visualize themselves performing a task in a safe way.

I've heard athletes claim they can improve their performance by practicing their skills mentally before actually performing. Some visualize an entire routine or sports competition in their mind's eye before their actual performance. Of course, they see themselves winning the contest and receiving the highest marks for their contributions!

My daughter is convinced, for example, that imagining herself making a free throw before shooting increases her chances of actually making the basket. Sports psychologists don't know whether this kind of mental imagery facilitates skill acquisition or only motivates the performer to try harder. But most are convinced mentally practicing a specific skill benefits actual performance (Murphy 1990). Thus, anything we do to help people see themselves mentally performing a safety-related activity should be good for *The Participation Factor*.

Set a Safe Example

A personal testimony is also influential because it's credible. After all, it describes a real experience. And if the testimony includes an example of the

Mental rehearsal can benefit actual performance.

safe behavior being advocated, the person giving the testimony becomes credible as an advocate of the desired behavior. My bicycle story not only illustrated that dangerous bike crashes can happen and bike helmets can prevent serious injury, it also made me credible as a proponent of bike-helmet use.

On several occasions, Mike has seen me before or after one of my biking sessions, and every time I was wearing a helmet. My consistent use of this protective device gives me authorization to promote the use of bike helmets. To be consistent with their message and to be a credible source of safety information, safety leaders are obligated to always set a safe example.

Recognizing Safety Achievement

People are more likely to participate in a certain activity when they feel good about themselves (self-esteem) and when they feel empowered (self-efficacy, personal control, and optimism). If done right, interpersonal recognition is probably the surest way to improve a person's self-image and belief in personal competence (self-efficacy). However, most of us haven't been taught how to give recognition effectively. Our common sense is not enough. Behavioral research has revealed strategies for making interpersonal recognition rewarding. Seven guidelines for giving quality recognition are listed in Figure 5.1. Let's consider each one.

Recognize as Soon as Possible

In order for recognition to provide optimal direction and support, it needs to be associated directly with the desired participation. People need to know what they did to earn the appreciation. If it's necessary to delay recognition, then the conversation should relive the recognized activity. Reliving the behavior means talking specifically about what warrants the attention. You could ask the person you're recognizing to describe aspects of the situation and the desirable behavior. This facilitates direction and motivation to continue the

Figure 5.1 Follow these seven guidelines when giving interpersonal recognition.

HOW TO GIVE SUPPORTIVE RECOGNITION

- *Recognize people during or immediately after safe behavior.*

- *Make it personal for both parties.*

- *Connect specific behavior with general higher-level praise.*

- *Deliver recognition privately.*

- *Let it stand alone and soak in.*

- *Use tangibles for symbolic value only.*

- *Realize the advantages of secondhand recognition.*

behavior. When you connect a person's participation with recognition, you also make the supportive conversation special and personal.

Make It Personal

Recognition is most meaningful when it's personal. Don't make the recognition so general it could fit anyone in any situation. Instead, customize it to fit a particular individual and circumstance. This happens naturally when the recognition is linked to specific behavior.

When you recognize someone, you are expressing personal thanks. It's tempting to say "we appreciate" rather than "I appreciate," and to refer to company gratitude instead of personal gratitude. Speaking for the company can come across as impersonal and insincere. Of course it's appropriate to reflect the individual's value to the organization when giving praise, but the focus should be personal. "I saw what you did to support our safety process and I really appreciate it. Your example illustrates actively caring and demonstrates the kind of leadership we need around here to achieve an injury-free workplace." The second statement illustrates the next guideline for quality recognition.

Add Higher-Level Praise

Recognition is most influential when it reflects a higher-order quality. Adding a universal attribute like leadership, integrity, trustworthiness, or actively caring to the recognition statement makes the recognition more rewarding and more likely to boost self-esteem and empowerment. State the specific behavior first, and then make a clear connection between the behavior and the positive attribute it reflects.

Deliver It Privately

Common sense tells us it's a good idea to recognize people in front of a group. This approach is used in athletic contests and disseminated by the pop psychology slogan, "Praise publicly and reprimand privately." Many managers give individual recognition at group meetings.

Isn't it maximally rewarding to be held up as an exemplar in front of one's peers? Not necessarily. Many people feel embarrassed when receiving special attention in a group. Some might actually avoid repeating the behavior they were recognized for in order to avoid being embarrassed again. I still remember the day my sixth-grade teacher recognized me in front of the class, and later four classmates beat me up on the playground.

Since quality recognition is personal and indicative of higher-order attributes, it needs to be delivered in private. After all, the recognition is special and relevant only to one person. So it will mean more and seem more genuine if it is given from one individual to another.

Let It Soak In

I've heard pop psychologists recommend a "sandwich method" for enhancing the impact of interpersonal communication. "First say something nice, then give corrective feedback, and then say something nice again." This approach might sound good, but it's not optimal. In fact, this mixed-message approach can cause confusion and actually reduce believability. The impact of initial recognition is canceled by the subsequent correction. Then the corrective feedback is neutralized by the closing recognition.

Keep interpersonal recognition simple and to the point. Give your behavior-based praise a chance to soak in. In this fast-paced age of trying to do more with less, we try to communicate as much as possible when we finally get in touch with a busy person. After recognizing a person's special safety effort, we are tempted to tag on a bunch of unrelated statements, even a request for additional behavior. This comes across as "I appreciate what you've done for safety, but I need more." Resist the temptation to do more than praise the good behavior you saw. If you have additional points to discuss, it's better to reconnect later, after your praise has had a chance to sink in and become a part of the person's self-talk.

Use Tangibles for Symbolic Value

As I discussed in Chapter 4, tangibles can detract from self-persuasion and the self-motivation aspect of quality recognition. If the focus of a recognition process is placed on a material reward, the words of appreciation can seem less significant. On the other hand, tangibles can add to the quality of interpersonal recognition if they are delivered as tokens of appreciation.

The benefit of your praise is weakened if the tangible is viewed as a pay-off for the safety-related behavior. But, if the tangible is seen as symbolic of special participation for safety, it strengthens the recognition. The most powerful tangibles display a slogan that promotes the purpose of the recognized behavior, like a T-shirt imprinted with "Safety Is a Core Value" or a ball cap displaying the term "Actively Care."

Use Secondhand Recognition

As I discussed in Chapter 4, people are sometimes suspicious of the genuineness of praise when it is delivered face-to-face. The praise receiver might feel there is an ulterior motive to the recognition—perhaps the praise deliverer expects a favor in return for special recognition (see illustration on page 67). Secondhand recognition, however, is not as easily tainted with this potential bias. Therefore, its genuineness is less suspect.

Suppose I tell you that someone else in your workgroup told me about the superb job you did conducting a safety audit. What is the impact of this secondhand recognition? Chances are you'll consider the recognition genuine because I was only reporting what someone else said. Because that person reported your success to me rather than you, I had no ulterior motive for praising you. Such secondhand recognition can build a sense of belonging or win-win teamwork among people. When you learn that someone was bragging about your behavior, your sense of friendship with that person will probably increase.

My main point here is that gossip can be good—*if it is positive.* When we talk about the participation of others in specific terms, we begin a cycle of positive communication that can motivate further involvement. It also helps to build an internal script for self-persuasion and sets an example for the kind of inter- and intrapersonal conversations that increase perceptions of empowerment, personal control, and optimism. As I explained in Chapters 2 and 4, these are person states that fuel *The Participation Factor.*

These guidelines for giving quality recognition are not exhaustive, but they cover the basics. Following them will increase the power of a conversation to facilitate participation. The most important point is that more recognition for involvement in occupational safety is needed in every organization, whether given firsthand or indirectly through positive gossip. And it takes but a few seconds to deliver quality recognition.

Receiving Recognition Well

Most of us get so little recognition from others that we are caught completely off guard when we get some appreciation. Some people claim they don't deserve the recognition. "Don't worry about it, I'm just doing my job." Others actually accuse the person giving recognition of being insincere or wanting something from them. "O.K., so what do you want from me?" This can be quite embarrassing, and may discourage people from giving more recognition.

Recall the basic motivational principle that the future occurrence of behavior is determined by its consequences. This is true for both the person giving recognition and the person receiving recognition. Quality recognition increases the participation recognized, and one's reaction to receiving recognition influences future recognition. Therefore, it's crucial to react appropriately when we receive recognition. Figure 5.2 lists seven basic guidelines for receiving recognition. Here's a rationale for each.

Avoid Denials and Disclaimers

We need to accept recognition without denial. Don't offer a disclaimer like "It really was nothing special," or "Just doing my job." And don't deflect the

HOW TO RECEIVE SUPPORTIVE RECOGNITION

- *Avoid denial and disclaimer statements.*

- *Listen actively with genuine appreciation.*

- *Relive recognition later for self-motivation.*

- *Show sincere appreciation.*

- *Recognize the person for recognizing you.*

- *Embrace the reciprocity principle.*

- *Ask for recognition when it is deserved but not forthcoming.*

Figure 5.2 Follow these seven guidelines when receiving interpersonal recognition.

credit to others with a reply like "I really could not have done it without your support" or "Other members of our team deserve more credit than I."

It's O.K. to show pride in your small-win accomplishments, even if others contributed to the successful outcome. After all, to achieve an injury-free workplace everyone must participate for occupational safety. In this context, everyone deserves periodic recognition. It's not "employee of the month," it's "employee of the moment."

Actively Listen with Genuine Appreciation

Listen attentively to the person giving you recognition. You want to know what you did right. You can also evaluate whether the recognition is given well. If the person says something general like "Nice job" without specifying a particular behavior, you might ask the person, "What did I do to deserve this?" This might help to improve that person's method of giving recognition.

It's important, of course, not to seem critical, but rather to show genuine appreciation for the special attention. Consider how difficult it is for most people to go out of their way to recognize others. Then revel in the fact you're receiving some of this rare recognition, even if its quality could be improved. Remember: A person who recognizes you is showing gratitude for what you do and will give more recognition throughout a work culture if you accept the recognition well.

Reflect on the Recognition Later

Most safety-related participation goes unnoticed. You do a lot for safety when no one else is around to show appreciation. Even when other people are available, they will probably not notice your extra effort because they are so preoccupied with their own routines. So when you finally receive some recognition, accept it as well-deserved. Remember the many times you've gone the extra mile for safety but didn't get noticed.

Listen intently to every word of praise, not only to show you care but also because you want to remember this special occasion. Don't hesitate to relive this moment later by talking to yourself. As covered in Chapter 4, such self-recognition can motivate you to continue your extra participation in safety.

Show Sincere Appreciation

After listening actively with humble acceptance, you need to show sincere gratitude with a smile and a "Thank you." Remember, your reaction to being recognized can determine whether similar recognition will occur again. So be prepared to reflect pleasure in the special conversation. I find it natural to add "You've made my day" to a "Thank you" because it's usually the truth. When people go out of their way to offer me quality recognition, they *have* made my day, and I often relive these occasions to improve a later day.

Recognize the Person for Recognizing You

As I explained above, your quality acceptance of praise can be rewarding to the person giving you recognition. This motivates that person to do more recognizing. Sometimes you can do even more to increase the occurrence of interpersonal recognition. You can recognize the person for recognizing you. In this case, you apply quality recognition principles to reward certain aspects of the supportive conversation.

You might say, for example, "I really appreciate your acknowledgment of specific behaviors. It shows you took the time to really see what I do around here for safety." This kind of rewarding feedback helps the person become more mindful of those aspects of the recognition process that are especially worthwhile.

Embrace the Reciprocity Principle

Sometimes people resist receiving recognition because they don't want to feel obligated to give recognition to others. This is the reciprocity principle at work. If we want to achieve an injury-free workplace, we need to embrace reciprocity as a norm. Research has shown that when you are nice to others, as when providing them with special praise, you increase the likelihood they will reciprocate by showing similar behavior (Cialdini 2001; Geller 1997a). You might not receive the returned favor, but someone will. I cover this principle in more detail in Chapter 7.

Bottom line: Your genuine acceptance of quality recognition will activate the reciprocity norm. The more this norm is activated from positive interpersonal conversation, the greater the frequency of interpersonal recognition. So accept recognition well, and embrace the reciprocity norm. The result will be more interpersonal involvement consistent with the vision of an injury-free workplace.

Ask for Recognition When Deserved

I have one final recommendation. If you feel you deserve recognition, ask for it. This might result in recognition viewed as less genuine than if it were spontaneous, but the outcome from such a request can be valuable. You might receive some words worth reliving later for self-motivation. More importantly, you will remind the other individual in a nice way that he or she missed a prime opportunity to offer quality recognition. This could be a useful learning experience for that person.

Consider the possible effects of your statement to another person that you are pleased with a certain result of your extra effort. With the right tone and body language, this won't seem like bragging, but only a declaration of pride in a personal accomplishment. The other person will probably support your self-recognition with sincere confirmation, and this will bolster your self-motivation. Moreover, you will teach the other person how to support the safety-related participation of others.

In Conclusion

The amount and quality of participation for safety in your organization is markedly influenced by how safety is talked about—from the managers' boardroom to the workers' break room. This chapter covered ways of using such interpersonal conversation to benefit *The Participation Factor*—from the words we use to discuss safety to giving and receiving personal recognition and corrective feedback. I also addressed the importance of intrapersonal conversation—a topic also examined in Chapter 4 as self-persuasion.

We often focus our interpersonal and intrapersonal conversations on the past. This helps us connect with others, but it also limits the potential for conversation to benefit participation. We enable progress when we move conversations with ourselves and others from past experiences to future possibilities and then to the development of a current action plan.

Expect people to protect their self-esteem with excuses for their past mistakes. Listen actively for barriers to safe behavior reflected in these excuses. Then help the conversation shift to a discussion of possibilities for improvement and personal commitment to apply a feasible action plan. This is often more likely to occur with a nondirective approach, in which more questions are asked than directives given. It's also useful to use opening words to protect the listener's self-esteem.

William James, the first renowned American psychologist, wrote, "The deepest principle in human nature is the craving to be appreciated" (from Carnegie 1936, p. 19). We all need to show more appreciation to others for their safety-focused participation, but most of us can improve the quality of our recognition delivery. In addition, we need to become more mindful of how we receive recognition from others, because how we do this determines the future frequency of more recognition—more fuel for *The Participation Factor.*

The Need for Competence

Safety involvement is not beyond the call of duty; it is the call of duty. That's the paradigm shift upon which this chapter is based. The notion is that working safely means working competently. Anything less is incompetent. Sell this perspective and you'll have buy-in for a basic tool that will improve the quality of safety-related participation— performance feedback. An effective performance appraisal process can provide this kind of feedback and thus fuel The Participation Factor in occupational safety. Yes, performance appraisals can be beneficial and appreciated by both those who give and receive them. This chapter shows you how to make that happen.

Do you assume people will not want to participate in your safety process? Why? Because it's inconvenient or time-consuming? Do you assume safety participation represents altruistic or sacrificial behavior, meaning it goes beyond self-interest? Why? Because the obvious consequences are rewards for other people and inconvenience for the participant?

I'd like you to consider an alternative perspective. I propose that people really want to participate—to play a role in keeping people safe. Consider that the opposite of active participation is incompetence, apathy, or helplessness. No one wants to be in those states.

Furthermore, I propose we stop talking about participation in a safety process as if it requires personal sacrifice—as if such behavior requires a relinquishing of personal gain so others might benefit. How many people can get excited about enduring negative consequences so others in the workplace might receive positive consequences?

Let's adopt the mindset that helping others reaps personal gains for *everyone* involved. Such behavior is not sacrificial or even unselfish. It rewards a basic human need to make a difference—to serve others. In other words, serving others is self-rewarding, not self-sacrificing. Consider that safety-related behavior is not "going beyond the call of duty"; rather it *is* the call of duty—anything less is incompetent.

People Want to Be Competent

Several researchers of human motivation have proposed that people naturally enjoy being able to solve problems and successfully complete worthwhile tasks (e.g., DeYoung 2000; Kaplan 2000; White 1959). In other words, we are motivated to learn, to discover, to explore possibilities, to understand what is going on, and to participate in achieving worthwhile goals. The label for this fundamental human motive is "competence."

Many motivational psychologists assume the desire for competence is self-initiating and self-rewarding. In other words, behavior that increases feelings of effectiveness is self-directed and does not need extrinsic reinforcement to keep it going. Furthermore, behavioral skills that increase competence are readily learned and practiced. What does this mean for *The Participation Factor*?

The Need for Self-Efficacy

I'm sure you see similarities between the need for competence and the self-efficacy belief addressed in Chapter 2. In fact, self-efficacy implies competence. Having self-efficacy means the participant believes she or he can organize and perform the procedures needed to achieve a desired goal. When people learn specific procedural steps for carrying out a certain safety process, they gain self-efficacy. They feel competent.

The Need for Response-Efficacy

You probably also recall another theme in Chapter 2—that self-efficacy is not sufficient to motivate participation. It's not enough to feel competent at a task; you need to believe your participation contributes to making a beneficial difference. Thus, effective training not only teaches step-by-step procedures, it includes a rationale for the usefulness of the process.

In safety, this translates to convincing the participants that applying the lessons learned will help people remain injury-free. Thus, the need to feel competent is satisfied by self-efficacy (believing one has the skills to implement a particular intervention) and response-efficacy (believing the intervention will have desirable impact).

The Power of Feedback

So how do we know we are competent at something? How do we know our competence makes a valuable difference? You know the answer—feedback. Feedback about our ongoing behavior tells us how we are doing and enables us to do better. We hone our skills through practice and behavior-based feedback. Sometimes this process feedback comes naturally, like when we see our behavior produce a desired result. But often, behavioral feedback requires careful and systematic observation by another individual—a trainer or coach —who later communicates his or her findings to the performer. In each case, feedback enables the development of self-efficacy and fulfillment of the need for competence.

Feedback about the results of a particular process—outcome feedback—supports the need for competence by showing desirable effects of participation. For example, a display of the percentages of safe behaviors among members of a work group indicates whether an interpersonal coaching process is working. When these percentages are graphed daily or weekly, a work group can track its progress at improving coaching competence.

Objective evidence of a reduction in injuries, property damage, or near-miss reports is, of course, the most rewarding feedback we can get in safety. This is the ultimate outcome feedback we work to achieve. Unfortunately, this feedback does not change rapidly enough to inform our competence. Also, this feedback can be invalid due to under-reporting. That's why we need ongoing behavior-based feedback to continuously build our self- and response-efficacy and satisfy our need for competence.

I've heard some behavior-based safety consultants argue that feedback is not a reinforcer. Technically, a reinforcer is a behavioral consequence that increases the frequency of the behavior it follows. So, if behavior does not improve after feedback, then the feedback was not a reinforcer. Likewise, praise, reprimands, bonus pay, or frequent flyer points are not reinforcers when they don't increase the frequency of the behavior they target; and they often don't.

Consider, however, that feedback delivered well, whether supportive, corrective or both, feeds the basic human desire to be competent. Feedback is not a payoff for doing the right thing. Rather, it is objective information a person uses to feel competent or to learn how to become more competent. There's no other consequence with greater potential to improve performance and thereby become a reinforcer.

Increased competence fuels *The Participation Factor*. In other words, when we *feel* more competent we're more likely to participate in the competence-relevant activities. And when we actually *are* more competent, the quality of our participation is naturally enhanced. So how can competence be increased and maintained? The most obvious answer to this question is behavior-based feedback and recognition, as addressed in Chapter 5.

To improve our competence we need feedback, and the most effective feedback is delivered soon after the occurrence of the behavior to be improved. Sometimes natural consequences provide feedback, like when we see the flight and landing location of a golf ball. Often, however, additional consequences are necessary to satisfy our need for more competence, as when a coach observes our golf swing and points out ways to improve.

Because humans can learn from feedback that occurs long after the occurrence of a target behavior, as when we read a book on golf swings, another common human relations technique can feed our need for competence. When delivered correctly, this technique can both direct and motivate behavior. I'm talking about the "performance appraisal," the theme of this chapter.

Why Most Performance Appraisals Fail

Does the prospect of completing, delivering, or receiving a performance appraisal turn you on? Do you view the performance appraisal as an opportunity to improve competence, either in yourself or someone else? Most employees, including my university colleagues, answer a vehement "no" to each of these questions. Why? Because most performance appraisals do not improve competence. They are designed and delivered ineffectively. Let's briefly review ten common pitfalls of many performance appraisals. Each characteristic of an ineffective performance appraisal suggests a specific improvement strategy.

Injury Rates Are Used to Evaluate Performance

Given that competence calls for safe performance, it's critical to include a safety metric as a performance-appraisal index. But outcome measures that reflect injuries are not very useful. Not only because they are reactive, but because they are usually unreliable. Plus, a focus on injuries as the key evaluation metric stifles the critical prevention process of reporting, discussing, and analyzing personal injuries (Geller 2001d; O'Brien 2000).

Instead, performance appraisals should include proactive safety process activities among their evaluation criteria. These include the important things organizations do to prevent property damage and personal injury, and obviously vary widely as a function of cultural, environmental, and individual factors.

They Are Completed and Delivered by Untrained Managers

When is the last time your organization conducted education/training seminars on the administration of performance appraisals? It's hard to believe

The annual subjective performance appraisal is not taken seriously.

most companies do not have a rigorous and regular course on the development, completion, and delivery of performance appraisals. As I show in this chapter, this competence-enhancement tool is not easy to use effectively.

Managers need to know how to conduct the several steps of an effective performance appraisal. They need to believe they can do it right (self-efficacy), and have confidence the tool will work to improve competence (response-efficacy). This usually requires substantial education, since most managers have had years of experience with ineffective performance appraisals— both delivering and receiving them.

They Require Excessive Paperwork

No one likes paperwork. Yet for many managers "performance appraisal" means paperwork. At my university, for example, every faculty member is required to complete a nine-page standardized survey for each of our six secretaries. We give numerical scores to each of several performance criteria and write justifications for our various rankings. These surveys are collected from our twenty-seven departmental faculty members and compiled. The scores for each criterion are averaged, and the commentaries are entered into a computer file. They are used by my department head to rank the secretaries and determine merit adjustments to each secretary's salary for the following year. This exemplifies two additional problems with standard performance appraisals, as explained next.

They Assign Numbers That Imply Ranking

Dr. Edwards Deming (1991, 1992) urged us to stop ranking people, yet we continue to attach numbers to evaluations that position individuals among others with regard to competence. Sometimes these numbers are used to determine salary or promotion—another characteristic of ineffective performance appraisals.

They Are Directly Linked to Financial Compensation or Promotion

The primary problem with using performance appraisals to rank employees and define their salaries is that such consequences compromise the purpose of the evaluation. They detract from the competence-building potential of the process. Numbers that can be used for financial compensation naturally activate defensiveness and bias, including the perception that any less-than-desirable evaluation is unfair. This can only interfere with constructive learning and competence improvement.

In addition, salaries are determined by factors immeasurable with a performance evaluation, especially an employee's "market value"—the relative difficulty an organization would experience if it attempted to find a replacement.

Thus, performance appraisals should not include numbers employees can use to compare their competence with others. The link between the results of a performance appraisal and an employee's salary should be indirect at best. Financial compensation should not be discussed during any aspect of a performance appraisal, from developing evaluation criteria to reporting the results.

Performance Criteria Are Developed by Managers

The criteria for a performance evaluation are usually defined by management. In fact, the typical performance appraisal form contains evaluation criteria defined years earlier but presumably applicable to everyone in the work force, or at least everyone with a given job title. Moreover, some of the criteria are impossible to evaluate objectively, as reflected in the next characteristic of ineffective performance appraisals.

They Include Generic Person States as Criteria

It's not uncommon for performance appraisal forms to list such desirable person states as "enthusiasm," "intrinsic motivation," "dependability," "loyalty," and "dedication," along with brief definitions of each criterion. Behavioral examples for a person state help one develop a consistent viewpoint of the criteria. However, rating an individual on such person dimensions requires subjective judgments that are essentially useless with regard to increasing a person's competence at a particular job. How can knowing one's ranking with regard to enthusiasm, motivation, dedication, or loyalty improve competence?

Effective performance appraisals include specific behavioral criteria (or objectives) customized for each employee. These evaluation objectives are defined by the individual employee, with advice and approval from the relevant manager or supervisor. Later in this chapter I address the development and delivery of individualized performance appraisals. Here my point is that generic subjective criteria lead to subjective evaluations that are ineffective with regard to improving competence.

They Are Completed Annually and Include No Progress Reviews

To be effective, a performance appraisal process must include periodic reviews of an individual's progress in achieving specific behavioral goals. Optimally, such progress reviews occur bimonthly, and might include revisions or additions to the list of goals. Then the annual performance appraisal becomes simply a summary or review of the progress reports, and perhaps a discussion of potential performance goals for the following year.

They Reflect One-Way, Top-Down Communication

The typical performance appraisal is a communication from manager to employee that in essence reflects the manager's opinion of the employee's performance. Sometimes this communication is only an impersonal written report, with no opportunity for the employee to enter an opinion. Often these reports contain critical commentary. Consider, for example, the criticisms listed in Figure 6.1, which are from actual performance evaluations.

I find the statements in Figure 6.1 quite humorous and actually descriptive of some people I know. But imagine how devastating any of these comments would be to the self-esteem and self-efficacy of the person receiving such a critique. We might use these to poke fun at another person, with the emphasis on "fun." But ponder receiving a negative comment like any of these on your formal performance appraisal form. How would that affect your *Participation Factor?*

- *His men would follow him anywhere, but only out of morbid curiosity.*

- *Works well when under constant supervision and cornered like a rat in a trap.*

- *When she opens her mouth, it seems that this is only to change whichever foot was previously in there.*

- *He would be out of his depth in a parking lot puddle.*

- *This young lady has delusions of adequacy.*

- *He sets low personal standards and then consistently fails to achieve them.*

- *This employee is depriving a village somewhere of an idiot.*

- *Got into the gene pool while the lifeguard wasn't watching.*

- *Got a full 6-pack, but lacks the plastic thingy to hold it all together.*

- *A photographic memory but with the lens cover glued on.*

- *Gates are down, the lights are flashing, but the train isn't coming.*

- *If brains were taxed, he'd get a rebate.*

- *It's hard to believe he beat out 1,000,000 other sperm.*

- *One neuron short of a synapse.*

- *Some drink from the fountain of knowledge; he only gargled.*

- *Takes him $1\frac{1}{2}$ hours to watch 60 Minutes.*

- *Wheel is turning, but the hamster is dead.*

Figure 6.1 What not to write on a performance evaluation.

The faculty members in my university department receive a confidential letter with rankings on four generic performance criteria by four to six members of the departmental executive committee. Specific and anonymous commentary from committee members are included, and not all of these statements are positive. The department head includes his rankings and a one-page summary of his opinion of the faculty member's performance in teaching, research, community/professional service, and outreach. I'm sure critiques are never as severe as the statements in Figure 6.1, but over the years

I have seen unflattering and unfair statements appear on these forms. For example, a department head once wrote on my evaluation, "Dr. Geller's reputation as an advocate for safety prevents him from being an objective researcher in this area."

We are invited to make an appointment with our department head for an interpersonal review of our evaluations, but these communications are generally one-way clarifications of the ranking process and various evaluation scores. Later we receive a confidential letter specifying our salary increase for the next academic year, presumably determined *entirely* by the performance appraisal process.

Little Reaction Is Solicited from the Employee

Many of my colleagues don't make an appointment to discuss their performance appraisals. Why should they? They expect a one-way communication that merely classifies or justifies their evaluation. The communication won't change anything or influence their next performance appraisal twelve months later.

In contrast, effective performance appraisals are two-way communications between employees who want to know specifically what they can do to improve their competence and supervisors who want to provide effective direction and motivation. As mentioned earlier, the end-of-the-year evaluation meeting is merely a summary of an employee's periodic progress reports, each of which solicits the employee's reactions.

It's beneficial to obtain an employee's written approval with each progress report, as well as with the annual summary. Signing a summary account of one's progress and prospects can increase commitment to follow through with future plans. It also provides documented evidence that a particular evaluation was accomplished and understood. Next I discuss procedures for making these two-way communications effective at cultivating commitment, confidence, and competence, thereby increasing the quality and quantity of participation.

Summary

Figure 6.2 summarizes the ten critical differences between ineffective and effective performance appraisals. Now let's move our discussion to techniques for developing and delivering an effective performance appraisal. The two most critical aspects of an effective performance evaluation are customizing appropriate performance goals and conducting constructive corrective-action discussions (Drake 1997; Murphy and Cleveland 1991). The first quality is key to developing a worthwhile performance appraisal, while the second is necessary for delivering the kind of performance evaluation that can improve an individual's competence.

INEFFECTIVE	EFFECTIVE
1. Injury report = criterion	1. Safety process = criterion
2. No training on delivery	2. Training on delivery
3. Excessive paperwork	3. Minimal paperwork
4. Numbers for ranking	4. No numerical score
5. Linked directly to salary	5. Linked indirectly to salary
6. Criteria set by manager	6. Criteria set by employee
7. Generic criteria	7. Customized criteria
8. Completed annually with no progress reviews	8. Periodic progress reviews summarized annually
9. One-way communication	9. Interactive communication
10. Employee reaction not obtained	10. Employee input solicited

Figure 6.2 Summary of the differences between ineffective and effective performance appraisals.

Defining Effective Performance Goals

When developed appropriately, performance goals guide and motivate individual participation. They are not general mission statements relevant for an entire work force, but rather are specific goals owned by an individual worker. Let's consider the characteristics of effective performance goals.

They Involve the Employee

If you want goals to direct and motivate performance, then the performer must take part in defining them. This should occur in a private conversation between a worker and his or her supervisor. The supervisor should certainly offer advice regarding the development of work goals, and must definitely approve the final list. But while it's appropriate for managers to suggest areas in which performance goals are needed and to offer suggestions, it's critical for the employee to perceive personal choice throughout this process.

They're SMART

The SMART acronym depicted in Figure 6.3 is an efficient and notable way to remember the essential qualities of effective goals: "S" for specific, "M" for motivational, "A" for attainable, "R" for relevant, and "T" for trackable. The common meanings for these terms are sufficient to guide successful goal setting, but note the connection of the three terms to the important beliefs I introduced in Chapter 2 and have referred to periodically throughout this book.

Specifically, *motivational* means that valuable consequences after reaching a performance goal are realized and deemed worth working for. This is the outcome-expectancy belief. Self-efficacy ("I can handle the assignment"), and response-efficacy ("The assignment will have beneficial impact") are necessary for competent performance and are implied by the *attainable* (for self-efficacy) and *relevant* (for response-efficacy) characteristics of SMART goals.

They Include Safety-Related Process Goals

To make performance appraisals relevant to occupational safety, it's critical to include one or more goals related to the prevention of personal injury. These should be specific process activities whose accomplishment will contribute to the vision of achieving an injury-free workplace. Thus, eliminating a certain number of injuries should never be a goal. Instead, SMART goals are set on important safety processes relevant to the individual's domain of responsibility and influence.

They're Achievable but Challenging

The individual should believe the goals are attainable (self-efficacy), but they should also be challenging. Some refer to these as "stretch goals." They manifest an expectancy that the individual can do better than average and implicate a need to periodically go beyond the call of duty—to do more than the norm.

Figure 6.3 Effective performance goals are SMART.

They're Flexible and Limited in Number

Having too many process goals can feel overwhelming and make individual goals less significant. Psychological research has shown that people can hold about seven numbers in working memory (Miller 1956), and therefore, it's unwise to define more than seven performance goals.

These SMART goals should be flexible—not "carved in stone." In other words, goals can be altered as circumstances change. For example, a particular goal could become less important, more challenging, or simpler to achieve than initially realized. How are goals refined? The answer is given by the final quality.

They Include Periodic Progress Reviews

Earlier in this chapter I indicated that effective performance appraisals include periodic reviews—progress reports—of an individual's accomplishment in reaching specific behavioral goals. These interpersonal conversations make or break the whole appraisal process. Revisions or additions to the list of performance goals occur in these meetings. Even more importantly, during progress reviews the employee receives competence-building feedback. The manager gives rewarding feedback to recognize and support specific successes and provides corrective feedback to pinpoint opportunities for improvement. Now let's review the basic qualities of an effective corrective feedback session.

Qualities of Effective Corrective Feedback

Since no one likes to be informed or reminded of personal failure, the corrective feedback or problem-solving aspect of a performance progress report is most challenging. Many managers shy away from this aspect of a performance appraisal, not only because they dislike negative interactions but also because they lack competence, real and perceived, at delivering corrective feedback.

As I indicated earlier in this chapter, most managers have not received training in this critical component of an effective performance appraisal system. Please consider carefully the following guidelines for delivering corrective feedback. They are relevant for every reader, since we all find ourselves in situations where correcting another person's behavior is called for.

Avoid Subjective or Judgmental Statements

Effective corrective feedback usually starts with the manager or supervisor explaining the problem or need for improvement. The problem should be described without judgmental comments. It's not useful to add subjective opinions at this point. Suggesting, for example, a problem resulted from poor judgment, insufficient motivation, or inadequate planning sets the wrong tone. It puts the employee on the defensive, precipitating a list of excuses for failure rather than ways to improve.

This discussion can initiate the development of a corrective action plan and sincere commitment to improve if the problem is stated objectively in terms of observable behaviors and the extrinsic context in which these behaviors occurred. Adopt the mindset that anyone could have demonstrated the inferior performance under similar circumstances. Then the challenge is to decide what environmental factors or conditions need to be changed in order to improve performance.

Learn the Employee's Perspective

Interpersonal conversation is biased by each person's previous experiences (see illustration below). It's really impossible to escape the impact of this

Communication is biased by personal experience.

premature bias in our conversations. Maintaining an open mind while listening intently before giving advice is the best way to limit this bias. In other words, attentive listening by the manager or supervisor encourages the employee to present his or her view of the problem and potential contributing factors.

The manager must sincerely want to understand the problem from the employee's perspective. This can happen only if the employee talks openly and discloses personal viewpoints. This is more likely to happen if the manager demonstrates actively-caring listening skills by a) showing authentic interest through body language, b) periodically restating the employee's point to reflect concern and check for understanding, and c) asking open-ended questions pertinent to the discussion.

Demonstrate Appreciation of the Employee's Perspective

Managers skilled at corrective feedback recognize the impact of selective perception referred to above and realize there's more than one way to view the same situation (see illustration on next page). As a result, they listen actively to develop an appreciation of the employee's perception of the problem. When managers show explicitly they understand the employee's outlook, they increase interpersonal trust and mutual respect. This increases the likelihood the employee will accept the need for improvement and work on a practical plan for corrective action.

Obtain Mutual Agreement

Managers who follow the first three guidelines bring the feedback discussion to a critical level—the point where both parties agree on the problem. Competence cannot improve unless the individual needing improvement recognizes and acknowledges the need. Thus, it's essential a consensus is reached regarding a need for performance enhancement. Then and only then can the next step be accomplished.

Discuss Potential Solutions and Select an Action Plan

This is obviously the problem-solving stage. Factors contributing to the problem and observable barriers to solving the problem are openly discussed. Some factors and/or barriers may be difficult or impossible to change. It might be necessary, in fact, to add supportive conditions in order to overcome obstacles or facilitate the occurrence of desirable behaviors.

Try not to be hampered by tunnel vision—a limited view of the situation. Develop a long list of potential solutions. Many may be currently impractical or unrealistic, but entertaining a broad range of ideal situations and compe-

*Perspective is
determined by
personal
position.*

tencies can lead to creative solutions. Select the best action plan for now, but recognize that a preferable solution may be feasible in the future.

Summarize the Plan for Corrective Action

Often a corrective feedback discussion ends with the manager reviewing his or her expectations. For many this might seem like the common-sense way to guarantee corrective action, but it's not. It's far better for the manager to ask the employee to summarize the performance-improvement plan mutually developed and agreed on. The manager listens for confusion or inconsistencies, asks for clarification, or offers refinements.

Obtain Commitment for Improvement

After the employee offers a clear statement of the corrective action plan, the manager has the perfect opportunity to solicit commitment. He should say something like, "It's obvious you know how to achieve a higher level of performance . . . do I have your commitment to make this happen?" Most employees will answer "yes" to the commitment question, but the nature of the prior conversation will determine the employee's empowerment to follow through.

Whether the employee goes beyond the call of duty to meet the new expectations depends on the degree to which the guidelines presented here are followed. As I discussed in Chapter 4, self-persuasion is key to personal commitment, and is increased by the perceptions of personal choice, ownership, and interpersonal trust occasioned by the corrective feedback discussion.

Review Progress

When people are self-persuaded, they feel personally responsible for achieving their goals. Such behavior is self-directed. This is the ideal outcome for a corrective feedback discussion, but don't count on this result. Much improvement is other-directed—motivated by an external accountability system.

Managers hold employees accountable for performance improvement through follow-up conversations that review progress. Optimally, this is viewed as an opportunity for an employee to show off accomplishment and for a manager to offer genuine appreciation and recognition, as covered in Chapter 5. This is also an opportunity for employees to request additional management support and perhaps to revise their goals. New circumstances may make it unrealistic to attain a certain goal. On the other hand, a particular goal could be reached early and a new one established.

Summary

The real benefit of a performance appraisal is not evaluation, but rather performance improvement. For this to occur, however, effective behavior-based goals must be created. And when these SMART goals are not met, corrective feedback must be delivered effectively. I have presented guidelines here for enabling these components of a performance appraisal system to build competence and benefit *The Participation Factor.*

It takes special one-on-one attention between supervisors and employees to accomplish effective performance appraisals. Anything less can be a complete waste of time and do more harm than good. So my advice is to cease doing performance appraisals at all if you can't follow the basic guidelines described here. But that's not enough. It's important to understand the role of certain factors that can render any performance evaluation unreliable and invalid, and therefore harm *The Participation Factor.*

Sources of Bias in Performance Appraisals

In this chapter I have presented ten critical differences between effective and ineffective performance appraisals and pinpointed two qualities of an effective performance appraisal that enable it to increase competence—individualized performance goals and constructive corrective feedback. Now let's consider six psychological factors that can prejudice the evaluation component of a performance appraisal. Becoming aware of these factors can limit their prominence and thus make the performance evaluation more accurate. Please realize, however, that performance appraisals used only for evaluation, as is the case with most, do not improve competence.

Leniency Error

This common type of error reflects an inclination to inflate everyone's performance evaluation (Hauenstein 1992; Murphy and Cleveland 1991). In other words, there's a tendency to evaluate everyone favorably. Why? Because managers want to avoid negative confrontations with employees who receive below-average ratings. Managers or supervisors want to avoid having to deal with an employee challenging a low evaluation on the grounds of an unfair assessment and biased judgment. And a strong case can usually be made for an unjust and corrupt evaluation unless the evaluation is free from subjective interpretation and based on periodic objective observations of the employee's behaviors.

However, if everyone gets a similar above-average score on a generic performance evaluation, the rating process is useless. This is a prime reason for eliminating the traditional evaluation and ranking component of a performance appraisal system, as covered above.

Halo or Devil Effect

A halo effect occurs when an initial positive impression of an individual leads to perceiving everything the person does in a favorable light. The opposite bias is termed a "devil effect" and occurs after we form a negative overall impression of a person and then are more attentive to negative than positive aspects of everything the person does (Murphy, Jako, and Anhalt 1993; Robbins and DeNisi 1994).

These biases occur because initial impressions usually have the most powerful impact and influence all subsequent observations of the individual. In other words, our perceptions of people are often biased by an attempt to confirm our first opinions of them. The consultant illustrated on the next page is trying to make a good first impression by wearing personal protection equipment, but he's off the mark. This failure at making a good first impression will likely handicap *The Participation Factor* throughout the entire session.

Initial impressions can result in a "halo effect" or a "devil effect."

The lesson here is twofold: Work hard to generate a positive initial impression in others, and try to observe others' performance as if you're seeing them for the first time. Recognize the fact that prior assessments of an individual predispose the way you see that person today. The next psychological factor biasing performance evaluations is directly relevant.

Affective Reaction

Affective—emotional—reactions toward the person being evaluated influence the evaluation. You've probably experienced this prejudicial variable many times. Perhaps you've tried explicitly to separate your personal feelings for an individual from an evaluation of that person's performance. A large amount of psychological research indicates that this is extremely difficult, even when raters are aware of their biases (Robbins and DeNisi 1994).

So your observations of another person's performance are influenced at least to some degree by your affective reaction to him or her. Exacerbating this problem, your formal evaluation of this person may occur days, weeks or months after your observations, allowing plenty of time for emotional feelings

126

to distort your memory of what you saw as well as your interpretation of the relevance, utility, and validity of what you remembered seeing.

Attributional Bias

This type of occurs when evaluations are influenced by perceived causes of performance, such as internal motivational factors. Suppose, for example, you need to evaluate two persons who, in your judgment, have achieved the same outcome level. However, you believe one of these individuals did not contribute a lot of effort but loafed along at half speed, coasting to the performance level you observed. In contrast, the other person is less talented and reached this level of output by working much harder. Would you give both of these individuals the same performance rating?

Research indicates that most people would assign a higher rating to the second worker—the one who put out the most effort and exceeded expectations (Mitchell, Green, and Wood 1982). Is this fair? Should effort count? If the evaluation is based on performance only, subjective attributional judgments are irrelevant and should not influence the assessment. Besides, attributional judgments are biased by a limited sampling of behavior and the observer's personal experiences. This leads logically to the next factor that sways interpersonal evaluations.

Attributions are biased by personal experience.

Similar-to-Me Error

Similar-to-me errors occur when raters assign higher ratings to persons similar to themselves in various areas than to people who are dissimilar (Baron 1998). Being human, we appreciate and like people who are similar to us. We can readily put ourselves in these people's shoes and understand (we think) their motivational attributions.

Thus, this bias links to the prior two factors—affective and attributional prejudice. That is, we are apt to like people who are similar to us. And when these people perform well, we are likely to attribute their behavior to positive internal motivation. After all, these people are similar to us, and we see ourselves as having more self-discipline and internal drive than most others in our work setting—right?

Stereotyping

Stereotyping occurs when evaluations are influenced to some degree by a person's membership in a particular social group. We tend to give global labels for people, such as student, patient, homosexual, union representative, safety professional, athlete, or homeless person. Each label prompts a particular image and a set of characteristics. Then the general label we give people influences how we view them, judge them, and react to their communication with us (Judd, Ryan, and Park 1991). The illustration below reflects a gender

Stereotypes are inaccurate and reflect mindlessness.

stereotype that in fact runs counter to statistics. As anyone who has purchased vehicle insurance knows, male drivers are more likely to experience a vehicle crash than female drivers.

Becoming more mindful of the vast differences among individuals and how these differences fluctuate according to time, place, and social context makes it difficult to attach labels to people (Langer 1989). Yet, let's face it, we do put people in categories. Such discrimination is even facilitated by popular personality tests like the Myers-Briggs Type Indicator (Myers and McCaulley 1985) and best selling books like *Men Are from Mars, Women Are from Venus* (Gray 1992). They contribute to the stereotyping bias, which can dramatically confound the evaluation component of a performance appraisal system.

Efforts to combat prejudice focus on teaching people that everyone should be considered equal and that categorizing people is wrong. In other words, to decrease discrimination and its accompanying problems, we are told to stop discriminating. Langer (1989) believes this is the wrong approach. Categorizing people and things according to discernable characteristics is a natural learning process. It's how we come to know and understand our surroundings.

The key to reducing prejudice and stereotyping is to make *more*, not fewer, distinctions between people. When people become more attentive to the numerous differences among individuals and understand how these differences vary according to the environmental or interpersonal context, it becomes increasingly difficult to put individuals into universal categories. It becomes impossible to view people and their behavior as black or white, normal or abnormal, masculine or feminine, safe or unsafe.

Has the mother in the illustration on the next page taken Langer's teaching to an ill-advised extreme? I wonder. Consider all the hate violence that occurs because people can't handle diversity. They haven't been adequately socialized to appreciate and respect people's differences.

In Conclusion

At the start of this chapter I called for a paradigm shift—a change in perspective about participating in safety efforts. Instead of calling on guilt or sacrifice to get people involved in procedures to eliminate hazards or decrease at-risk behavior, I suggest we assume people are naturally motivated to make beneficial differences. People hate feeling incompetent or helpless. They want to learn, to discover, to become more proficient at worthwhile tasks. People want opportunities to ask questions, to study pertinent material, to work with people who know more than they, and to receive feedback that can improve their competence.

It doesn't have to be Venus or Mars.

Therefore, participation in occupational safety is not a thankless job requiring self-sacrifice or a special degree of altruism. Safety participation puts people in control of environmental and human factors that can cause serious injury or death. Safety participation avoids one of the most aversive human states—the feeling of incompetence or helplessness.

Participation in an effective safety process provides opportunities to satisfy a basic human need—the need for competence. The effective and frequent delivery of behavior-based feedback provides a mechanism for improving the quality of safety participation as well as cultivating feelings of competence throughout a work culture.

Chapter 5 presented guidelines for delivering behavior-focused feedback and recognition during one-on-one conversations with coworkers. This chapter showed how performance appraisals can be used to provide constructive feedback for improving a person's competence. First, I defined ten problems with the typical performance appraisal system used by most corporations in order to introduce qualities of a competence-building performance appraisal.

Then I focused on the two critical components of an effective performance appraisal—customizing performance goals and delivering corrective feedback.

The real benefit of a performance appraisal is not evaluation, but rather performance improvement. For this to occur, however, SMART behavioral goals must be created; and when these goals are not met, corrective feedback must be delivered effectively. It takes unique one-on-one conversations between supervisors and employees to accomplish this.

This is not easy or efficient. There's no quick fix, and there's no middle ground. A performance appraisal that does not approximate the guidelines I presented here can do more harm than good. In addition, the six biasing factors presented in the latter portion of this chapter need to be minimized. When it comes to evaluating human performance in an attempt to improve competence, do it right or don't do it at all. The effective performance appraisal provides potent fuel for *The Participation Factor*. Additional support can be found in the social dynamics of a situation—the focus of the next chapter.

7

"Don't criticize them; they are just what we would be under similar circumstances."

—Abraham Lincoln

The Support of Social Dynamics

Do you realize how much you're influenced by the social dynamics of daily circumstances? This chapter teaches you six fundamental social influence principles and explains how each can be an advantage or disadvantage to The Participation Factor *in occupational safety. You'll be introduced to an innovative survey you can take to determine your own social influence profile. Knowing how various social dynamics affect your own attitudes and behaviors allows you to overcome their undesirable effects. Such insight also enables you to increase your ability to get more people involved in attaining and sustaining an injury-free workplace.*

We are social animals. Social relationships define who we are, how we feel, and what we want. We participate with and for other people on a daily basis. Often our motivation to participate comes from others, whether we're working alone or on a team. Plus, the value of what we purchase with our earnings, from the clothes we wear to the vehicles we drive and the homes we maintain, is determined in large part by the opinions of others.

Whether we're completing a job assignment or competing in an athletic contest, people's reactions to our behavior determine whether we feel competent or incompetent at participating. As a result, all the person factors I've described so far in this book, including self-esteem, self-efficacy, response-efficacy, outcome-expectancy, personal control, stress, distress, optimism, and belonging, are influenced significantly by other people. I'm talking about social dynamics—the focus of scientific study by social psychologists. Social psychology is "the scientific study of how people think about, influence, and relate to others" (Taylor, Peplau, and Sears 2000, p. 3).

I'm sure you see the relevance of social psychology to occupational safety in general and *The Participation Factor* in particular. Participation in occupational safety is facilitated or inhibited by the various social dynamics of a work culture. The challenge of developing the kinds of interdependent relationships needed to achieve an injury-free workplace is dependent on a number of social influence principles. These are explained and illustrated in this chapter. With these social psychology principles and procedures you'll be able to analyze the interpersonal factors hindering optimal involvement in safety and decide which can and should be changed to fuel *The Participation Factor*.

We begin with a discussion of six social influence factors and their ramifications in occupational safety. Then I introduce, for the first time, a scale my students and I developed to measure an individual's relative inclination to be affected by each type of social influence. You can take the test, score it using the straightforward instructions, and graph your own social influence profile. Actually you might want to page ahead and take the Social Influence Survey (SIS) now, before learning any more about these principles. Then your score will be a more valid measure of your social influence profile. More importantly, taking the SIS and defining your social profile now will surely motivate you to read the explanation of each principle.

I must make clear that the SIS is new, and has not been adequately tested for predictive validity. The SIS is the result of two years of development, including factor analysis and reliability tests of earlier versions. Thus, we are confident the SIS accomplishes an accurate classification of people's influence tendencies according to the definitions given here of each social influence principle. We cannot say, however, what it means to have a certain SIS profile. We don't know what kinds of behavior are predicted by various SIS scores. My students and I are currently conducting research to find this out.

At this point, the SIS is at best a useful teaching tool. It gets people interested in learning more about the social influence principles and their relationship to *The Participation Factor* in occupational safety. Actually, the idea that people have different social influence profiles is innovative, and will not be accepted by social psychologists without substantial research with the SIS.

Social psychologists present these influence principles and related behavior-change strategies as affecting everyone. There is no discussion in the research literature about some principles having greater impact than others or about individuals responding differently to them. Thus, even the idea of an SIS is novel, let alone the fact that such a scale can provide valid classifications of individual differences.

So please take and score the SIS with these caveats in mind. Use it with colleagues and friends to get them interested in learning about social influence and *The Participation Factor*. Then you can teach them what follows next. We start with a discussion of a social influence principle I've already introduced in Chapter 4. Our initial research with the SIS suggests this one is generally the most appreciated and influential.

Consistency: We Try to Be Consistent in Thought and Deed

Many psychologists consider the consistency principle a weapon of influence lying deep within us and directing our everyday actions. It reflects our motivation to be (and appear) consistent. Simply put, when we make a choice or take a stand, we encounter personal and social pressures to perform consistently with our commitment (see the illustration on page 73).

We obtain this pressure to be consistent from three basic sources: 1) society values consistency in people, 2) consistent conduct is beneficial to daily existence, and 3) a consistent orientation allows for shortcuts in information processing and decision making (Cialdini 2001). Instead of considering all relevant information in a certain situation, people need only remember their commitment or decision and respond consistently. This principle explains people's resistance to change, while also suggesting particular ways to motivate lasting improvement in both behavior and attitude.

Seek Public and Voluntary Commitment

When people sign their name to a petition or pledge card, they are making a commitment to behave in a certain way. Later, they behave in this way to be consistent with their commitment. Safety professionals can use this variation of the consistency principle to increase various safety-related behaviors (Geller and Lehman 1991). After a discussion about a particular work procedure, for example, the audience could be asked to make a commitment to perform the desired behavior. What kind of commitment should be requested?

Commitments are most effective (or influential) when they are public, require some effort, and are perceived as voluntary (not coerced). Thus, it would be more beneficial to have employees make a public rather than private commitment to perform a certain safe behavior. And, it would be better to have them sign their name to a card or public declaration display than to merely raise their hand. In addition, it's very important that those pledging to follow a certain work practice believe they made the commitment voluntarily.

The reality might be that decisions to make a public commitment are dramatically influenced by external factors like peer pressure. But as discussed in Chapter 4, too much external pressure can be detrimental because of the decrease in self-persuasion and self-direction. When people write an internal script saying they made a personal choice, consistency is most likely to follow the commitment. Thus, the promoters of a commitment strategy need to appreciate the self-persuasion concept and realize the influence of personal choice. Then they will make statements that allow participants to believe the commitment is not coerced but is up to them.

Figure 7.1 shows a sample promise card for using the consistency principle to increase participation in a safety process. The behavior targeted to increase in frequency could be selected by a safety director or group leader or through a group consensus discussion. This behavior is written on the promise card, perhaps by each individual in a group. Group members decide on the duration of the promise period and write the beginning and end dates on the card. Then each group member should be encouraged to sign and date the card. I have found this group application of the "safe behavior promise" strengthens a sense of group cohesion or belonging as well as facilitating participation. Follow these procedural points for optimal results:

- Define the desired target behavior specifically.
- Involve the group in discussing the personal and group value of the target behavior.
- Make the commitment for a specified period of time that is challenging but not overwhelming.
- Assure everyone that signing the card is only a personal commitment, not a company contract.
- Allow no penalties (not even criticism) for breaking a promise.
- Encourage everyone to sign the card, but do not use pressure tactics.
- Encourage signers to keep their promise cards in their possession or to post them in their work areas as a reminder.

Figure 7.1 The safe behavior promise card uses the consistency principle to increase participation.

SAFE BEHAVIOR PROMISE CARD

I promise to_____

_____

_____

From _____ until _____

_____
SIGNATURE   DATE

Start Small and Build

Sometimes referred to as the "foot-in-the-door" technique (Freedman and Fraser 1966), this influence strategy also follows directly from the consistency principle. To be consistent, a person who follows a small request is likely to comply with a larger request later. Thus, after agreeing to serve on a "safety steering committee," an individual is more willing to give a safety presentation at a plantwide safety and health meeting. Research has found this commitment strategy to be successful in boosting product sales, monetary contributions to charities, and blood donations (Geller 2001d).

The promise-card technique described above uses this principle. More specifically, after people sign a pledge card that commits them to perform a certain behavior for a specified period of time (such as "Buckle vehicle safety belts for one month," "Use particular personal protective equipment for two months," "Walk behind yellow lines for the rest of the year"), they are more likely to actually do the safe behavior.

The "foot-in-the-door" technique only works to increase safe behaviors when people comply with the initial small request. In fact, if a person says "No" to the first request, this individual might find it even easier to refuse a

After a foot-in-the-door we expect more.

subsequent, more important request. Thus, if you receive a "No" in answer to your request, you didn't start small enough. In this case, you should be prepared to retreat to a less demanding request. I describe this technique later under the reciprocity principle.

Raise the Stakes Later

This technique occurs when a person is persuaded to make a decision or commitment (for example, to serve on the plant safety steering committee) because of the relatively low stakes associated with the decision (the monthly safety meetings will not require too much time and effort). Then, when the individual gets committed to the decision (for example, attends the first two safety meetings), the stakes are raised (more meetings are requested for a special safety effort). Because of the consistency principle, the individual will be likely to stick with the original decision (remain an active member of the committee).

More than twenty years ago, Robert Cialdini and colleagues (1978) first demonstrated the powerful influence of this technique when attempting to get college students to sign up for an early (7:00 A.M.) experiment on "thinking processes." During the solicitation phone calls, the 7:00 A.M. start time was mentioned up front for half the subjects. Only 24 percent of these individuals agreed to participate. For the other subjects, the caller first asked if they wanted to participate in the study. Then, after 56 percent agreed, the caller raised the stakes and said the experiment started at 7:00 A.M. The caller gave subjects a chance to change their minds, but none did. Furthermore, 95 percent of these individuals actually showed up at the 7:00 A.M. appointment time. After making an initial commitment to participate, practically all of the subjects showed consistency and kept their commitment—in spite of the higher stakes.

This procedure is similar to the "foot-in-the-door" technique in that a larger request occurs after the target person agrees with a smaller request. A key difference, however, is that there is only one basic decision in this procedure, with the costs or stakes raised after initial commitment. This compliance tactic is common among car dealers. Once a customer has agreed to purchase a car at a special price (for example, $800 below all other competitors), the price is raised for a number of reasons. The salesperson's boss might have refused to approve the deal, certain options had not been included in the special price, or the dealership manager may have decreased the value of the customer's trade-in.

Customers who have agreed to the special price will usually not change their minds with a price increase, because reneging on a purchase decision may suggest a lack of consistency or indicate failure to fulfill an obligation (even though the obligation is only imaginary). Often customers will develop a set of new reasons to justify their initial choice and the additional costs.

This influence strategy is illustrated below. After the couple is seated in an elegant restaurant and begins reading the menu, the waiter brings in a wine list. If they had dealt with congested traffic or waited in line for an opportunity to dine at this particular restaurant, that extra effort increases commitment and makes it more likely an expensive wine will be selected.

Don't Stifle Trust

The stakes-raising strategy raises a critical issue with regard to using certain techniques to increase safe behavior. Even though this influence strategy is used rather frequently to increase compliance, how would you feel about change agents (people who use the technique) if you knew they used the procedure intentionally to get more money, commitment or participation from you? For example, do you trust the waiter who brings you a list of expensive wines only after you've been seated and made selections from the food menu? Your answer probably depends on whether you believe that sequence of events was performed intentionally to get you to buy more.

When the stakes are raised we feel obligated to pay.

Similarly, you might not dislike or mistrust the car salesman who adds cost to a vehicle's advertised purchase price unless you are suspicious the price differential was fabricated deliberately to increase revenue. In other words, our trust, appreciation, or respect for people might decrease considerably if we believe they have intentionally used a particular influence technique to trick or deceive us into modifying our attitude or behavior. Of course, there may be no harm done if the result is clearly for our own good (as for our health or safety) and we realize this.

Which First—Attitude or Behavior?

Because of the consistency principle, it doesn't matter whether attitude or behavior changes first. The issue is whether a technique is available to influence one or the other. The three influence techniques discussed under the consistency principle were introduced as ways to target behavior. However, it could be argued that internal (attitudinal) dimensions were intertwined throughout each technique. For maximum influence, for example, the pledge-card procedure requires the person to believe (internally) that the commitment was voluntary. Following successive compliance with escalating demands, internal commitment is developed, until eventually an "attitude" results.

In addition, the stakes-raising technique depends on the target individual developing an internal justification (through self-persuasion) for the initial decision, which then strengthens commitment and leads to behavior following the additional cost or effort required. Consequently, the key lesson is that people attempt to keep their internal person state (like attitude) and external participation (or behavior) consistent. Thus, whether attitude or behavior is influenced first, the other will probably follow, if the person does not feel coerced.

Reciprocity: We Reciprocate to Return a Favor

Some psychologists, sociologists, and anthropologists consider reciprocity a universal norm which motivates a lot of interpersonal behavior. It can be used to increase people's involvement in a safety-improvement process and to cultivate interdependence. Simply put, the reciprocity principle is reflected in the slogan "Do for me and I'll do for you." In other words, if you are nice to someone, he or she will feel obligated to return the favor. Research has shown that the favor might be returned to someone other than the original source (Berkowitz and Daniels 1964).

I witnessed the reciprocity norm rather dramatically when I worked in the Virginia prison system in the mid-1970s. In this setting, several inmates used gifts and other forms of personal assistance to dominate other inmates. I knew an inmate, for example, who went to great lengths to place a gift in the cell of a new inmate he wanted to dominate. Accepting such a gift meant the target inmate (or victim) was now obligated to return a favor in order to save face.

Have you ever felt uncomfortable after someone did you a favor? I certainly have felt this way and I interpret my discomfort as the reciprocity principle in action. Another person's favor makes me feel obligated to reciprocate. What does this mean for safety management? I think it means we should look for opportunities to go out of our way for another person's safety. When we actively care for someone else's safety, we increase the likelihood they will actively care for the safety of someone else.

It's important to realize that how we react to people after doing them a favor can either stifle or mobilize reciprocity. When a person thanks you for participating in a safety process you should not demean the favor by saying things like "No problem," or "It was really nothing." Anything that makes the participation seem insignificant or trivial will reduce the impetus for reciprocity. However, adding words to make the involvement appear more significant or meaningful can be quite awkward and create an uncomfortable or embarrassing situation.

To maintain a comfortable verbal exchange that does not demean participation and inhibit reciprocity, you could react to someone's "Thank you for participating" with something like, "Thank you, but I know you'd do the same for me." This reaction shows admiration for the thank you, and thus increases the likelihood more thanks will be given. Plus, it activates the reciprocity principle in a way that will be perceived as genuine and valid.

I'm sure you recognize that this social influence principle also operates in undesirable directions, as in getting even with someone for their apparent malice. It's probably a primary cause of "road rage." For example, what is your reaction when another vehicle "aggressively" cuts in front of you without signaling? As illustrated on the next page, you should use self-dialogue to avoid negative emotions that can escalate to road rage. At least that's what the clinical psychologists and psychotherapists tell us (Larson 1996, 1999; Nerenberg 1995). But the reciprocity principle tells us something else. Feeling protected in their own vehicles, many drivers have an urge to return the disfavor.

Intention probably plays a critical role here and in other situations relevant to the reciprocity principle. Drivers who feel the need to retaliate perceive an aggressive driving maneuver as intentional. If victims of aggressive driving could convince themselves the infraction was unintentional or "accidental," the reciprocity principle would probably have much less impact. Similarly, if someone's good deed is viewed as mindless or fortuitous, the sense of obligation to return the favor should be minimal. I say "should" in the prior sentence because social psychologists have yet to study how intention or mindfulness can influence the reciprocity principle.

Road rage reflects undesirable effects of the reciprocity principle.

We also don't know how time affects the reciprocity principle. Common sense tells us that the obligation to return a favor is strongest immediately after receiving a person's good deed. Likewise, the need to retaliate for risky and aggressive driving is greatest immediately after the incident. However, you probably know someone, if not yourself, who relives a good deed, along with relevant indebtedness, long after it occurs. Plus, there are numerous "Hatfield and McCoy" stories where a single conflict between individuals and families established retaliatory sentiments that lasted for years and even generations.

The reciprocity situation illustrated on the next page depicts both intentionality and durability. Again, without research addressing these issues, we can only speculate from our own experiences. However, we can be quite sure that this social influence principle does noticeably affect much interpersonal behavior, both desirable and undesirable. Our challenge, of course, is to get this principle used for more safe than at-risk behavior.

Gifts Aren't Free

Has someone ever influenced you to listen to a sales pitch after giving you a gift? Have you ever felt obligated to contribute to a charity after receiving gummed personal address labels and a stamped envelope for your check? Have you ever purchased a certain food in a supermarket after eating a free sample? Did you ever feel obliged to purchase a commodity after using it for a ten-day "free" trial period? Did you ever contribute to the Hare Krishna Society after a Krishna member gave you a flower at an airport? If you answered "yes" to any of these questions, it's likely you have been influenced by the *reciprocity principle*. Many marketing or sales-promotion efforts count on this "free sample" approach to influence purchasing behavior.

In one experiment, Isen and Levin (1972) observed that 84 percent of those individuals who found a dime in the coin-return slot of a public phone (placed there by researchers) helped the researchers' accomplice pick up papers he dropped in the subject's vicinity. In contrast, only 4 percent of those who did not find a dime helped the man pick up his papers. Similarly, students given

The impact of reciprocity can last a long time.

a cookie while studying at a university library were more likely than those not given a cookie to agree to help another person by participating in a psychology experiment (Isen and Levin 1972).

Does this justify the distribution of gifts for promoting safety, such as pens, T-shirts, caps, cups, and other trinkets? Yes, to some extent, but the amount of reciprocity activated depends on the recipient's perceptions. How special is the gift? Was the gift given to a select group of people, or was it distributed to everyone? Does the gift or its delivery represent significant sacrifice in money, time, or effort? Can the gift be purchased elsewhere, or does the safety slogan on it make it special?

The bottom line here is that the more "special" the safety gift—as perceived by the recipient—the more reciprocity is activated. Remember also that the way a safety gift is presented can make all the difference in the world. The labels and slogans linked with the gift can influence the amount and kind of reciprocity implied. If the gift represents the participation expected from an "elite" group, a special type of reciprocity is activated. These people tell themselves they are considered safety leaders, and then they need to justify this label by continuing their extra participation for the safety of others.

Door-in-the-Face: Start Big and Retreat

Suppose the plant safety director pulls you aside and asks you to chair the safety steering committee for the next two years. Let's assume you perceive this request as outrageous, given your other commitments and the fact you have never even served on a safety steering committee before—let alone chaired one. You say, "Thanks for asking, but no." The safety director says he understands, and then asks whether you'd be willing to serve on the committee. According to social psychology research, because the safety director "backed down" from his initial request, you will feel subtle pressure to make a similar concession—to reciprocate—and agree to the second, less demanding assignment.

Dr. Robert Cialdini and associates (1975) were among the first to demonstrate the influence power of this "door-in-the-face" technique. Posing as representatives of the "County Youth Counseling Program," they approached college students walking on campus and asked them to volunteer to chaperon a group of juvenile delinquents on a day trip to the zoo. When this was the first and only request, only 17 percent of those approached volunteered to help.

However, three times as many students volunteered when the researchers first asked for a much larger favor. Specifically, they asked whether the student would be willing to counsel juvenile delinquents for two hours a week over a two-year period. All subjects refused this request, but then half of them agreed to serve as unpaid chaperons for a day at the zoo. Apparently, the researchers' willingness to retreat from their initial request influenced several college students to reciprocate and comply with a smaller favor.

Have you ever wondered why lawyers ask for such outlandish amounts of money at the start of a civil trial? Or why labor negotiators start with extreme demands? It's likely these influence agents do not expect to receive their initial request, but perhaps they've learned they are more apt to succeed with a second request after retreating from the first. They've learned the power of this reciprocity-based technique through real-world negotiation. Or, it's possible some lawyers never learned firsthand the advantage of beginning negotiations high but do this because that's what their colleagues do. In this case, they are influenced by the conformity principle, which we turn to next.

Conformity: We Follow the Crowd

In classic research conducted by Solomon Asch and associates in the mid-1950s, more than 33 percent of intelligent and well-intentioned college students were willing to publicly deny reality in order to be consistent with the obviously inaccurate judgments of their peers. This innovative approach to studying conformity (Asch 1951) involved six to nine individuals sitting around a table and repeating aloud their judgment of which of three comparison lines was the same length as a standard line. All but the last individual to voice a decision in sequence were research associates posing as subjects. On some trials, the research associates uniformly gave obviously incorrect judgments.

The correct answer was always obvious, and on several trials everyone gave the correct answer. On some trials, however, an obviously incorrect comparison line was selected by each research associate according to plan, and the critical question was whether the subject would deny the obvious truth in order to conform with the group.

This and similar procedures have been used in numerous social psychology experiments to study the social dynamics that influence amount of conformity. For example, a subject's willingness to deny reality in order to go along with the group consensus was facilitated by increasing group size (Asch 1955) or the apparent competence or status of group members (Crutchfield 1955). On the other hand, the presence of one dissenter (or nonconformist) in the group was enough to significantly decrease conformity. For example, a subject's selection of the correct line increased significantly when the earlier decision of only one of fifteen research associates reflected the correct choice (Nemeth 1986).

The phenomenon of social conformity is certainly not new to any reader. We see examples of conformity every day, from the types of clothes people wear to their particular styles of communication in both written correspondence and verbal presentation. The male illustrated below is using this principle in an attempt to influence more participation from his companion. Thus, the role of conformity as a factor influencing at-risk behavior cannot be overlooked. Plus, we need to realize that group pressure to conform, even to conform with at-risk behavior, is greater when the group is larger and the group members are perceived as relatively competent or experienced.

Conformity and Observational Learning

This principle of social influence is similar to the basic behavioral safety concept of "modeling." Modeling—observational learning—simply means we learn by watching other people, and we teach others by our example. When the safe example is demonstrated by the majority of workers, the consistency principle kicks in to influence similar participation from others. Of course, we also learn at-risk behavior by observing others, and such behavior is maintained when our peer group practices the same risky behavior in our presence.

When peers perform there's pressure to conform.

The following anecdote illustrates an undesirable but humorous outcome from observational learning. It reminds us how much children learn from their parents without their parents' awareness. Indeed, socialization is often a subtle process whereby behavior is learned through observation and maintained by the consensus of one's peer group. Here's the story. I was told it actually happened.

> When Dad came into his daughter's bedroom, she requested, "Daddy—would you tuck me in like you do Mommy every night?" He said, "Sure, honey," and pulled the covers up underneath his daughter's chin. As he left the room his daughter called after him, saying, "Wait Daddy—would you give me a goodnight kiss like you do Mommy every night?" Dad said, "Sure, honey," and he kissed his daughter on her cheek. As he was leaving the room again, his daughter called after him with one more request: "Daddy . . . Daddy wait . . . would you whisper in my ear like you do Mommy's every night?" "Sure, honey," he replied, and he leaned down and went "Bzzz, Bzzz, Bzzz" in his daughter's ear. Then she said, "Not tonight, Daddy, I have a terrible headache."

Our actions influence others to a greater extent than we imagine. Without us being aware of our influence, our children learn by watching us at home, and our coworkers are influenced by our practices at work.

Macho Independence

As illustrated on the next page, we are all influenced by what we see people do on television, especially people to whom we can relate. In addition, conformity and observational learning can influence a resistance to look out for the safety of others. There are some common attitudes and behaviors that really get in the way. For example, I often encounter a group of workers who have learned a kind of macho, tough-guy consensus about safety. Over the years, they've come to believe safety is a personal matter. You know the attitude: "It's my own business if I want to take a risk. It's bad enough the company is on me all the time. Now I have to get it from you? I know what I'm doing, so get out of my face, please."

If these people see a hazard in someone else's work area, they leave it alone. It's not their responsibility. Besides, they don't want to insult or anger the person by mentioning it or taking care of it. You see, that's the social norm they've developed by watching others and following the crowd. Rugged individualism instead of belonging and interdependence. That's the perspective negative peer pressure is working to maintain. It's very destructive. It can result in a lot of at-risk behavior, overlooked hazards, and needless injuries.

We model what we see others do on television.

The We/They Norm

How about work cultures where the social norm is we/they? For those folks, caring about safety is almost like consorting with the enemy. Who do they think the enemy is? Well, sometimes it's the government. They see safety as something OSHA makes people do against their will. Sometimes the company or management is seen as the enemy. In a milder form, people feel the company is not really concerned about their personal safety. "They're just interested in keeping the injury numbers down or keeping their costs down to an acceptable level. They don't really care whether I get hurt or my buddy gets hurt, so why should we help them with their numbers?" In an atmosphere like that, peers can make you feel out of place if you go beyond the call of duty for safety.

In the worst kind of we/they situation, workers regard safety as a top-down control process, as I discussed in Chapter 1. "Do as I say or be punished." In this situation workers feel controlled, so there's a lot of peer pressure to "beat the system." People actually encourage each other to take risks—the important thing is not to get caught.

Power of Dissension

Once a macho, win/lose attitude takes hold, it can be hard to change. People feel very comfortable doing stuff just because "everyone else does it." Conformity to social norms is a strong motivator. So if that's your situation, try to remember it took some time for the negative peer pressure to build up. It's going to take time to change it. But it *can* change. It starts by a few people deviating from the norm and setting a safe example.

Social conformity research has shown that one dissenter—a leader willing to ignore group pressure and do the right thing—is enough to prevent others from succumbing to social conformity. When this dissenter has authority in the situation, many others will also follow suit. This is explained by the next basic principle of social influence.

Authority: We Obey Those in Charge

In classic research conducted by Stanley Milgram and associates in the 1960s, 65 percent of intelligent and well-meaning college students followed orders to administer 450-volt electric shocks to a screaming peer. Imagine you are one of nearly a thousand participants in one of Milgram's twenty obedience studies at Yale University. You and another individual are led to a laboratory to participate in a human learning experiment. First, you draw slips of paper out of a hat to determine randomly who will be the "teacher" and who will be the "learner." You get to be the teacher.

The learner is taken to an adjacent room and strapped to a chair wired through the wall to an electric shock machine containing thirty switches with labels ranging from "15 volts—light shock" to "450 volts—severe shock." You sit behind this shock generator, and you're instructed to punish the learner for making errors in the learning task by delivering brief electric shocks.

You're instructed to start with the 15-volt switch and move up to the next higher voltage every time the learner makes a mistake. You do as you're told, and you hear the learner moan as you flick the third, fourth, and fifth switches. When you get to the eighth switch, labeled "120 volts," the learner yells, "These shocks are painful." And when you flick the tenth switch the learner shouts, "Get me out of here!"

At this point, you might think about stopping, but the experimenter says, "Please continue—the experiment requires that you continue." So you do. And when you reach the 330-volt level, you hear shrieks of pain. The learner pounds on the wall, and then becomes silent. Still, the experimenter urges you to flick the 450-volt switch when the learner fails to respond to the next question.

At what point do you think you would refuse to obey the experimenter's instructions? If you believe you'd stop playing this sadistic game soon after the learner indicated the shock was painful, your prediction would be the same as people Milgram surveyed before conducting the experiment, including forty psychiatrists. So even Milgram (1963) was surprised that 65 percent of his actual subjects, ranging in age from twenty to fifty, complied fully with the experimenter's requests—right up to the last 450-volt switch.

Why did they keep going along? Did they figure out the learner was really part of the research team and wasn't really receiving shocks? Did they realize they were being deceived in order to test their obedience to authority? No— all subjects displayed genuine concern and distress when giving the shocks. They sweated, trembled, and bit their lips when they were giving the shocks. Some laughed nervously. A few openly questioned the experimenter's instructions, but most did exactly what they were told to do.

As with the conformity research, Milgram and associates studied the influence of various situational factors on the amount of obedience. Full obedience exceeded 65 percent (with as many as 93 percent flicking the highest shock switch) when 1) the authority figure (i.e., the one giving the orders) was in the

Following orders to give electric shocks was not a pleasant experience.

room with the subject, 2) the authority figure was supported by a prestigious institution (such as Yale University), 3) the shocks were given by a group of "teachers" in disguise to remain anonymous, 4) there was no evidence of deviance (i.e., no other subject was observed disobeying the experimenter), and 5) the victim ("learner") was depersonalized or distanced from the subject (i.e., in another room).

According to Stanley Milgram himself, an important lesson from this research is that "Ordinary people, simply doing their jobs, and without any particular hostility on their part, can become agents in a terrible destructive process" (Milgram 1974, p. 6). In a similar vein, people might perform unsafe acts or overlook obvious safety hazards and put themselves and others at risk as a result of social obedience or social conformity. The statement, "I was just following orders" reflects this obedience phenomenon, and "Everyone else does it" implies conformity or peer pressure.

Passing the Buck

The subjects in Milgram's experiments had learned from childhood to follow authority—from "mother knows best" to "the boss knows best." This allowed them to escape taking personal responsibility for what they were doing. If someone in authority tells you to do something, you're willing to do it because if something goes wrong, it's not your fault. You can blame the person who told you to do it. Sometimes we use authority as an excuse. Think about it. When we were kids and we got into trouble, we were quick to say, "It's not my fault, she told me to do it."

It's not hard to see what all of this has to do with safety in the workplace. We need to be aware of the power of authority and encourage people to resist the temptation to follow orders blindly. There are times when a supervisor might actually ask a worker to perform a behavior that could endanger the worker, other coworkers, or the environment. It's not supposed to happen, of course, but it does.

Sometimes it's unintentional, because the person giving the order does not fully understand the safety requirements of the job. But sometimes it's done intentionally. To get a job done faster a supervisor might encourage at-risk behavior. The supervisor might have learned over the years that the behavior is never followed by an injury. You know—it's the supervisory version of the "it won't happen to me" perspective I discussed in Chapter 3. It's the "it won't happen to you" attitude. Whenever a job assignment puts a person at risk for personal injury, we need to support workers when they show the personal responsibility to resist and do the right thing for safety.

Conformity and Authority

This and the previous social influence principle—social conformity—go hand in hand to affect *The Participation Factor.* The statement "I was just following orders" reflects obedience to authority, and "Everyone else does it" reflects conformity or peer pressure. As safety leaders, we need to realize the powerful impact of both conformity and authority and plan interventions to overcome their potential negative influence. Remember that a person who deviates from the norm and sets a safe example can decrease undesirable conformity and obedience. Of course, some employees command more authority than others, and the qualities of these leaders are addressed in the next chapter. Authority is often determined by job title or hierarchical position in the company. But seemingly insignificant characteristics of an individual can signal authoritative influence (see illustration below).

Ingratiation: We Participate for People We Like

For whom would you most likely actively care—someone you dislike or someone you like? The answer is obvious and reflects the value of increasing our personal appeal to others when cultivating interdependency and a Total Safety Culture. Social psychology research has verified a number of intuitive techniques to facilitate ingratiation, including:

A variety of factors signal authoritative influence.

- Demonstrate agreement with an individual on other matters before making a request.

- Offer genuine one-to-one praise, recognition, or rewarding feedback as discussed in Chapter 5.

- Use "name dropping" to show association with people respected by target persons.

- Radiate positive nonverbal cues such as smiles and friendly gestures that show appreciation and interest in the other person.

- Modify your personal appearance to be more acceptable and appealing to the other person(s) as exaggerated in the illustration below. Realistically, this might mean, for example, donning or removing a tie in order to appear more similar to a target audience (recall the unsuccessful attempt to do this by the consultant in the illustration on page 126).

- Use people's names when you address them.

Unlikes don't attract; rather similarities are appealing.

What's In a Name?

The last point is the simplest and most basic, but it could be the most important. It's a primary principle in the Dale Carnegie seminars on "Winning friends and influencing people" (Carnegie 1936). We know intuitively the value of remembering a person's name, yet we often forget the dearest word to everyone's ears. We all do this. We forget a person's name at critical times and attempt a cover-up with general impersonal statements like "How are you?" "How's it going?" "It's been a long time, and you haven't changed a bit." All the while we're searching our memory bank for the person's name, because we realize that using the person's name would make the conversation much more personal and friendly.

It doesn't take long to forget a person's name. How many times, for example, have you been introduced to a person and before the end of a brief conversation you lose the name? The more you get into the conversation, the more you want to know the individual's name. Also, the longer the conversation, the more embarrassing it is to ask, "What's your name again?"

What can we do about this common problem? First, recognize that it's common. It happens to everyone who doesn't repeat the person's name to themselves or actually say the person's name during the conversation. So those are two prime strategies for remembering a name, with the second technique working best. Not only does using the individual's name in the

It's the dearest word to our ears.

conversation decrease the chances you'll forget it, it also makes the conversation seem more personal and special to the other person. Dale Carnegie was right: "A person's name is to that person the sweetest and most important sound in any language" (Carnegie 1936, p. 86).

How often do you receive phone calls from people who introduce themselves at the start but by the end of the conversation you've forgotten their name? The remedy for this is easy. Simply get in the habit of writing down the person's name immediately. This strategy should not stop you from using the person's name intermittently throughout the conversation. But having a record of the caller's name enables you to avoid that awkward statement we hear so often at the end of a lengthy phone conversation with a stranger: "What's your name again?"

Naming Group Members

How important is it for discussion facilitators or instructors to learn the names of participants in a training course, professional development seminar, or team meeting? The answer is obvious. Calling on people by first name in a group meeting can do wonders to make the entire session more pleasant, as well as increase the amount of individual participation throughout the session. That's why I'm so pleased to see name tags on tables in group meetings. It's especially useful when I can read the names from the front of the room. When I can't, I merely walk closer to the location of a relevant name tag and use the person's name when appropriate.

It's amazing how much more I enjoy leading a training session when I can call on people by name. Similarly, my classes at Virginia Tech seem much more pleasant after I learn the names of my students. When I address participants by name, I feel more personable toward the group, and I stimulate more verbal participation as a result. And when I get questions and comments from my audience, I can customize the presentation and make it more special for the group.

If name tags are not available, I ask everyone to introduce themselves at the start of the session and I write the names on a seating chart. Sometimes I have the opportunity to make a seating chart before the session begins by consulting with someone who knows the participants. Then I can call on people by name, and with some rehearsal during breaks, I can attach names to faces. It sometimes helps to associate an individual's name with his or her features, expressions, or general appearance. Often I can link something about a person to someone else in my long-term memory bank with the same name. The result—I feel better about the entire session or class, and I'm convinced the group members feel better about me.

The Value of the Handshake

How important is the handshake in forming initial impressions of people? It's the one way we reach out physically to touch someone. Often it's the first and last time we actually use our sense of touch to know someone. And what do we know? Have you formed a good or bad impression of a person on the basis of a simple handshake?

Have you ever received a "fish" or "wimp" handshake and immediately thought negatively about the person you're meeting? Or perhaps you've thought less of a person following a crushing "Superman" handshake. Here's the most important question: "How many times have *you* given a feeble or crushing handshake that hampered ingratiation?"

When I ask audiences these questions, almost everyone's hand goes up to indicate they've received of both kinds of undesirable handshakes. But no one admits to *giving* wimpy handshakes. Then comes the critical question: "How do you know?" How do you know your handshake does not appear too weak or too strong to the other person? When's the last time you shook someone's hand and asked, "How was it?"

That last question provokes laughter from my audiences, and it probably seems silly to you. But think about it. You can't know how your handshake comes across unless you get feedback. Without specific feedback about your handshake, you don't know whether your handshake makes a good, bad, or indifferent initial impression.

Given the crucial importance of the handshake in forming initial impressions, you should really ask for feedback about your handshake from a close friend—one you can count on to be open and honest and willing to be critical about your performance. Ask this person to rate your handshake on a scale of one to ten, with "one" being awful and "ten" being ideal. When your friend gives you an "8.5," ask the follow-up question, "What can I do to reach a perfect ten?" Then practice the suggestions to develop the optimal handshake for benefiting ingratiation and *The Participation Factor*.

The Power of Recognition

This ingratiation principle is paramount in the dating game. And of course, genuine interpersonal recognition or social approval is key. In Chapter 5, I gave a number of guidelines for giving and receiving recognition. Here I only want to point out the special value of recognition in increasing ingratiation and spreading a sense of belonging and interdependency throughout a work culture. When you recognize a person appropriately, you do more than support that person's desirable participation and build his or her self-efficacy and self-esteem. You influence that person to like and appreciate you more, and this increases your ability to exert positive social influence on that person.

156

Ingratiation occurs frequently during "the dating game."

And that's not all. Not only does liking and appreciation increase from the person being recognized to the person doing the recognizing, the reverse also happens. After all, when you find behavior to recognize, you learn to appreciate the person performing the desired behavior. This mutual ingratiation increases feelings of belonging and interdependency. Then, through the power of reciprocity, one appropriate recognition interaction will be likely to lead to more interpersonal recognition. This in turn causes more ingratiation and interdependency throughout a work culture.

Too often we experience the opposite of ingratiation when it comes to safety. Safety management is often a confrontation between an authoritative employee and a subordinate who is not following a rule. Or, requests to serve on a safety steering committee or special safety task force are given in an impersonal memo or by e-mail. Although we understand the principle of ingratiation through personal experience, we often don't follow it when soliciting involvement in occupational safety.

Safety is often presented as a top-down condition of employment, and this leads to the perception that we follow safety rules because we "have to" not because we "want to." As I detailed in Chapter 4, this can limit our perception of freedom and choice when it comes to safety. As discussed under the final social influence principle, this reduced sense of personal freedom or control can lead to counterproductive behaviors and attitudes.

Scarcity: It Increases Value

I wrote an initial draft of this chapter while on a five-day speaking tour in California for CareAmerica. It was ironic that when I got to this final part of the manuscript, I was in the midst of experiencing the very essence of this principle. To make a long story short, the airline misplaced my luggage on my Sunday trip from Pittsburgh to San Francisco. As a result, I spent the first two days and nights with only the clothes on my back.

It was truly amazing how valuable my luggage became in the context of such deprivation. I literally spent hours on the telephone attempting to locate my luggage. After my Monday presentation in Sacramento, I traveled back to the San Francisco airport to check on the whereabouts of my "valuable" luggage. How excited I became when I learned it had been found (in New Bern, North Carolina) and would be delivered to my room at the Embassy Suites that evening. That night I anxiously awaited a phone call to tell me my luggage was at the front desk. I even declined an opportunity to go out for dinner so I could be there when my luggage arrived. My luggage had become so valuable that I wanted to get it as soon as possible.

My luggage didn't arrive that night, and I slept restlessly in anticipation of the critical phone call. Could it be I must wear the same "traveling" clothes for a third day and a second presentation? Just before I left my room the next morning for breakfast—in my only available clothes—I got a phone call from the front desk. My luggage was there, and I was thrilled. I skipped breakfast in order to have enough time to retrieve my luggage and change clothes before my speech.

Readers who have not suffered such a lost-luggage incident have certainly experienced the scarcity principle in other situations. Have you ever gone out of your way to purchase front-row tickets to a sports event or music concert? Have you ever jammed into a department store to take advantage of a "special, limited-time" bargain? Or, maybe you're a collector of rare coins, stamps, baseball cards, or antique furniture. Have you ever bid against someone at an auction for a one-of-a-kind item? Scarce items become even more valuable when other people want them. Have you ever paid more than a fair price at an auction in order to win a bidding competition? Each of these situations illustrates how the value of something increases with perceived scarcity.

The Forbidden Fruit Phenomenon

Why do teenagers consume drugs, including alcohol, cigarettes, and marijuana? The principle of social conformity (or peer pressure) discussed above is certainly a factor, but why is the purchase and consumption of these drugs considered valuable? They don't taste good, at least at first, and everyone knows they're not good for you. For years these teens have heard the slogan "Just say no to drugs." Why is it difficult for some teenagers (and adults) to say "No"?

Consider that the message "Say no," when heard repeatedly, can actually make the drug seem desirable. It's the "forbidden fruit" phenomenon, as told in the biblical story of Adam and Eve in the Garden of Eden. Forbidding something makes that something seem valuable, and if we can beat the system to partake of the "forbidden fruit," we might experience an extra rush of pleasure because we asserted our freedom in a top-down situation we perceived as inhibiting our individuality and creativity.

Items or opportunities that appear scarce in the eyes of the beholder seem more valuable. Thus, drugs seem desirable to some because they are scarce, and consuming drugs can feel more pleasurable because the behavior itself represents a scarce freedom. I'm not advocating the legalization of drugs or the lowering of the legal age for alcohol consumption. But understanding the scarcity principle can help us appreciate why certain illegal acts occur and why increased enforcement of laws does not help to develop individual values.

Reacting with Counter-Participation

When individuality or perceived personal control is made scarce with top-down control, some people will exert contrary behavior in an attempt to assert their freedom. This was discussed in Chapter 4 and illustrated on page 69. This phenomenon is referred to as "psychological reactance" by social psychologists (Brehm 1966, 1972) and "countercontrol" by behavior analysts (Skinner 1971). Whatever you call it, the results can be devastating to *The Participation Factor*. Perhaps we should call this reaction to command and control "counter-participation."

I met a guy once who wore safety frames. That's right, not safety glasses, only safety frames. He had removed the lenses. When a supervisor walked up the aisle, the employee would look right at him and wave. His coworkers gave him lots of peer support for thumbing his nose at the system. They perceived safety as a top-down mandate that restricted their individual freedom. This worker increased his status in that culture by pushing against the system and demonstrating his independence. Recall the earlier discussion of the we/they norm under the conformity principle.

Here's another real-world story of top-down control influencing "counter-participation." Not too long ago, a top manager at a large oil refining company noticed an operator not wearing his hard hat. When he asked the worker about this, the individual touched the top of his head and said, "Oh, I didn't realize that. I felt a hat on my head (a baseball cap) and thought it was a hard hat." This manager, figuring he had uncovered a "root cause" of noncompliance with hard-hat policy, distributed memos and posted signs announcing a new policy: "No baseball caps allowed." The outcome of this well-intentioned attempt at a quick fix is illustrated below.

Thus, situations that appear to take away personal freedom or control can activate participation opposite to what we want. When people perceive the system as restrictive, they might attempt to beat it. When the threat of punitive consequences is severe and the probability of getting caught high, most people will comply. But compliance will typically be limited to situations in which the rule is enforced. Don't expect people to internalize the rule and follow it when they don't have to. As emphasized in Chapter 4, the more control you exert on the outside of a person, the less control the person develops on the inside.

Top-down control can provoke counter-participation. True participation can't be dictated.

The Social Influence Survey (SIS)

Figure 7.2 is a forty-nine-item survey that assesses a person's relative inclination to be affected by each of the six social influence principles described in this chapter. As I explained earlier, this scale is new and has not yet been adequately tested for validity. However, the questions do reliably differentiate the six social influence principles, and therefore the SIS can be used as a tool to teach the social dynamics of safety. Earlier in this chapter I suggested that you take this survey before reading about the six social influence principles in order to increase the probability the SIS can provide you with an unbiased "social influence profile."

Scoring the SIS

The SIS is easy to score and interpret. I've found it very useful to ask participants in a seminar on social dynamics to take the SIS at the beginning of my class and score it. Then, with their social influence profile in front of them, the participants are eager to learn about each social influence principle and its relevance for occupational safety.

After circling a number next to each statement on the SIS, transfer the numbers circled to the appropriate boxes of the scoring table in Figure 7.3. You'll note that the forty-nine numbers in the table, corresponding to the respective item numbers of the SIS, appear in consecutive order from left to right. Thus, it's very convenient to transfer the number circled for each item to the appropriate box.

For each number marked with an asterisk (*) in the table (items 12, 18, 19, 26, 33, 35, 39, 42, 47, and 49), subtract the number you circled for that item from eight, and write the result in the appropriate box. Calculate the totals for each of the seven columns in the table by adding the box scores vertically, and write the totals in the seven boxes across from the label "Totals."

Obviously, the higher the total in a given column, the more relevant the particular social influence principle is for you. The score itself is unimportant, however; what's important is the relative ranking of the six principles. The sum of the *first six* column totals is meaningful as an overall indicator of your propensity to be influenced by social dynamics in general. But we have not yet developed norms for the SIS, so I can't tell you what a particular total score means relative to scores of other people. It might be interesting, however, for you to compare your scores with those of colleagues, friends, and family members. At least you'll generate some stimulating conversation about social influence.

The Denial Factor

If you have completed and scored the SIS, you undoubtedly have questions about the last column—"Denial." This is not a social influence principle but rather a measure of the truthfulness or believability of your answers. A

Figure 7.2 The Social Influence Survey (SIS)

Please read each question carefully and circle the number that indicates your level of agreement or disagreement with each statement: 1=Strongly Disagree (SD); 2=Disagree (D); 3=Mildly Disagree (MD); 4=Neutral (N); 5=Mildly Agree (MA); 6=Agree (A); 7=Strongly Agree (SA).

	SD	D	MD	N	MA	A	SA
1. I have a reputation for being true to my word.	1	2	3	4	5	6	7
2. When someone does me a favor, I want to return the favor.	1	2	3	4	5	6	7
3. When I meet new people at work, I do whatever it takes to win their favor.	1	2	3	4	5	6	7
4. I sometimes go along with the group decision, even when I think it's wrong.	1	2	3	4	5	6	7
5. I always try to follow the rules.	1	2	3	4	5	6	7
6. I would be likely to attend a grand opening of a store for the one-time-only deals.	1	2	3	4	5	6	7
7. I am never jealous of other people.	1	2	3	4	5	6	7
8. When I pledge to do something, it gets done.	1	2	3	4	5	6	7
9. If a stranger helps me when I'm in need, I'm more likely to help another stranger in need.	1	2	3	4	5	6	7
10. When I meet people with power over me, one of my main goals is to get them to like me.	1	2	3	4	5	6	7
11. I would put up with some discomfort to fit in with my group.	1	2	3	4	5	6	7
12. It is more fun to break the rules.	1	2	3	4	5	6	7
13. I like buying one-of-a-kind items and/or collectables.	1	2	3	4	5	6	7
14. I never complain when things don't go my way.	1	2	3	4	5	6	7
15. Once I have committed to something, I won't back out.	1	2	3	4	5	6	7
16. I treat others as I like to be treated.	1	2	3	4	5	6	7
17. I volunteer for jobs that will gain me the approval of others.	1	2	3	4	5	6	7
18. I speak up about my opinions, even when they are unpopular.	1	2	3	4	5	6	7
19. I make fun of police.	1	2	3	4	5	6	7
20. I like being the only one with an item that everyone wants.	1	2	3	4	5	6	7
21. I never have a bad day.	1	2	3	4	5	6	7
22. Being reliable is important to me.	1	2	3	4	5	6	7
23. When people compliment me, I usually give them a compliment.	1	2	3	4	5	6	7
24. I would do a job I hated to gain respect and/or admiration from people who might be in a position to help me someday.	1	2	3	4	5	6	7
25. I will change my beliefs to agree with other people I like.	1	2	3	4	5	6	7
26. I believe in the statement, "Rules were made to be broken."	1	2	3	4	5	6	7
27. I try to pack as many fun things as possible into the last day of vacation.	1	2	3	4	5	6	7
28. I never criticize others behind their backs.	1	2	3	4	5	6	7
29. My friends know they can count on me.	1	2	3	4	5	6	7
30. When people are nice to me, I am more likely to be nice to them.	1	2	3	4	5	6	7

	SD	D	MD	N	MA	A	SA
31. I avoid confrontations with others I work with because I might need a favor from one of them someday.	1	2	3	4	5	6	7
32. It's hard for me to make up my mind about a TV show until I know what others think.	1	2	3	4	5	6	7
33. When I get "no" for an answer after I ask permission to do something, I do it anyway if I can get away with it.	1	2	3	4	5	6	7
34. I don't mind paying more for something that is unique.	1	2	3	4	5	6	7
35. I get angry every now and then.	1	2	3	4	5	6	7
36. I keep my appointments.	1	2	3	4	5	6	7
37. If I receive a birthday card from someone, I make sure I give them a card for their birthday.	1	2	3	4	5	6	7
38. I would do more than my fair share to impress others.	1	2	3	4	5	6	7
39. I would rather be myself than pretend to be someone I am not to please others.	1	2	3	4	5	6	7
40. I obey laws even if I don't agree with them.	1	2	3	4	5	6	7
41. I would skip work if I thought it was going to be one of the last beautiful days of summer.	1	2	3	4	5	6	7
42. Those who are closest to me sometimes get upset with me.	1	2	3	4	5	6	7
43. I finish what I start.	1	2	3	4	5	6	7
44. If I am shown true kindness, I try to be kind in return.	1	2	3	4	5	6	7
45. I think being liked by others with influence over me is important.	1	2	3	4	5	6	7
46. It is better to get along than to rock the boat.	1	2	3	4	5	6	7
47. I sympathize with rebels.	1	2	3	4	5	6	7
48. "Carpe diem" (Seize the day) is a motto I try to live by.	1	2	3	4	5	6	7
49. I sometimes do things I regret later.	1	2	3	4	5	6	7

Figure 7.3 Scoring table for the Social Influence Survey.

Consistency	Reciprocity	Ingratiation	Conformity	Authority	Scarcity	Denial
1	2	3	4	5	6	7
8	9	10	11	12 *	13	14
15	16	17	18 *	19 *	20	21
22	23	24	25	26 *	27	28
29	30	31	32	33 *	34	35 *
36	37	38	39 *	40	41	42 *
43	44	45	46	47 *	48	49 *
TOTALS						

relatively high total in this column (thirty-five or above) indicates that your answers on the entire SIS are very biased and are probably invalid.

More specifically, scoring high on the Denial items means you agreed to questions that the average person would not agree to if they were being completely frank and truthful. You can go back to the statements classified as Denial items and see what I mean. People who want to give a good impression (as in the ingratiation principle) would agree with the Denial items, which in most cases indicates an overly idealistic (or less than truthful) response.

A high Denial score could also reflect mindlessness when completing the SIS. In other words, the respondent might not have been thinking carefully when completing the SIS, or may have misunderstood the instructions or misused the seven-point evaluation scale. At any rate, consider the accuracy of an SIS profile highly suspect if the Denial score is thirty-five or above.

Your Social Influence Profile

Figure 7.4 is a graph you can use to plot your social influence profile. Simply place a dot above each of the six social influence principles and the Denial column according to the totals in the bottom row of the table in Figure 7.3. Then connect the dots. The first six points reveal your social influence profile, and the last point reflects bias—the lower this last point, the better. What does this profile mean?

Figure 7.4 Graph on which to plot your social influence scores.

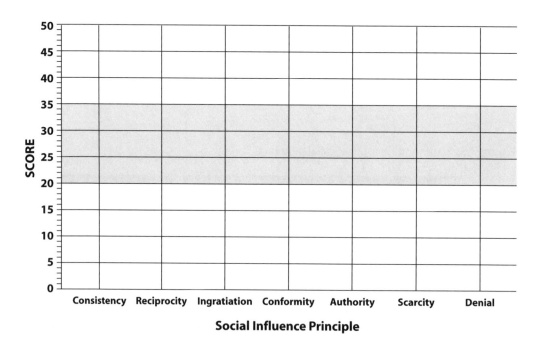

Given the limited research we've done with the SIS, I urge you to consider only the relative differences among your six influence scores. In other words, the shape of your graph is meaningful or diagnostic but the absolute level of any score is not. The shape of your profile indicates the relative prominence of the six social influence principles in your current life "state." I say "state," not "trait," here, because I believe the profile discloses only a temporary ranking of the social influence principles in your life. It's likely that maturity, learning, and various life experiences will change your social influence profile. Thus, you should not view the SIS graph as a permanent picture of social influence in your life, but rather a snapshot of the relative importance of these principles for you *today*.

Our current research with the SIS is examining the stability of the social influence profile. You could do this for yourself by taking the SIS several months and a year from now and comparing profiles. Of course, you realize that your scores will be biased by your knowledge of the SIS and what you expect or want to discover in the comparisons.

To date, our research with the SIS has shown quite convincingly that the social influence profiles vary markedly from individual to individual. This might not be surprising to you or seem important; but note that before we created the SIS, individual differences were not linked to social influence. Social psychologists typically talk about these principles as generally influencing everyone, without considering whether certain principles are more powerful than others or whether individuals vary with regard to their propensity to be influenced by the six principles.

Figure 7.5 depicts the average social influence profile of 235 males and 223 females who took my introductory psychology class last spring (2001). You can see that the Consistency principle was most popular and the Confority principle was least popular for this sample. There were also significant gender differences. Specifically, the average overall score for women (225.5) was significantly higher than that of men (220.1), and women scored significantly higher than men in Consistency, Reciprocity, Authority, and Scarcity. In addition, the men's Denial scores were significantly higher than the women's, meaning the men in this sample were more likely to be untruthful or mindless when completing the SIS. "Of course," say my female readers. "Tell me something I didn't already know."

Figure 7.6 compares the average social influence profile of 458 university students versus 46 safety professionals, consultants, or hourly workers attending my social dynamics seminar at a Utility Safety Conference held in Atlanta, Georgia. Both samples were obtained in the spring of 2001. Both profiles are relatively high in Consistency and low in Conformity. Significant differences were found in the Consistency, Authority, and Scarcity categories, with the most prominent difference occurring in Authority. Perhaps you're not surprised that people attending a safety conference would score substantially higher on Authority than the average college student, but for me it's gratifying to demonstrate expected individual differences with the SIS. These findings support the validity of our scale, indicate potential for follow-up research with the SIS, and suggest substantial promise for integrating individual differences with social influence.

You might find it interesting and informative to compare your social influence profile with the mean profiles graphed in Figures 7.5 and 7.6. Is your total influence score higher or lower than the average university student? Does your profile match more closely that of the university student or the participant at the safety conference?

It's probable your profile is quite different from any of those displayed here. After all, the profiles in Figures 7.5 and 7.6 are averages, and your profile is one of a kind. Remember also, there is no good or bad profile. The social influence profile only suggests a ranking of the relative importance of six social influence principles in your life today.

I hope this exercise has piqued your interest in the social dynamics of safety and motivated you to teach the six influence principles to others. Please consider copying the SIS (Figure 7.2) and the scoring table (Figure 7.3), and using them as a teaching tool. If you find any intriguing differences between

Figure 7.5 Mean SIS profile of male (n=235) vs. female (n=223) university students taking introductory psychology in the spring of 2001.

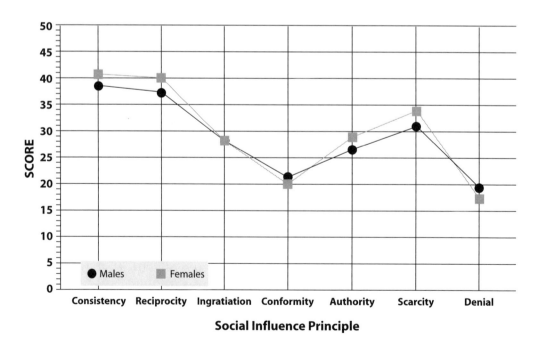

various social influence profiles, I'd love to hear from you. Our research with the SIS has only just begun, and we could benefit greatly from your input. There is so much to learn about the interaction of individual differences and the social dynamics of safety.

In Conclusion

A key point in Chapter 1 was that the achievement of an injury-free work-place requires a transformation from dependency and independency to *inter*dependency. In other words, it's not enough for people to rely on the company to keep them safe through engineering intervention. Nor is it suffi-cient for people to count only on their own individual effort to keep them free from injury. Rather, people need others to remove environmental haz-ards they don't notice and to provide corrective feedback for at-risk behavior they might not realize they're performing. Such interdependency requires interpersonal interaction. The social dynamics of the situation determine whether such exchanges are likely to occur and whether the impact of such interaction will be beneficial or detrimental to safety.

The social dynamics of an organization reflect the culture and influence the culture at the same time. That is, certain aspects of a work setting affect social

Figure 7.6 Mean SIS profile of university students in spring 2001 (n=458) vs. attendees at the author's seminar on the social dynamics of safety at the spring 2001 Utility Safety Conference (n=46).

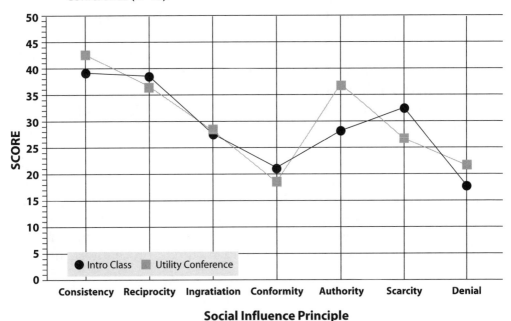

dynamics, and these social dynamics in turn alter the culture. The six social influence principles described in this chapter expose basic social dynamics. They can inhibit or facilitate participation for occupational safety.

Our desire to be *consistent* influences resistance to change. But when people choose to change even a little, the consistency principle can facilitate more commitment and more beneficial change. With this principle in effect, small increases in participation can result in supportive attitude change, followed by more participation and more desired attitude change. This spiraling—participation feeding attitude, feeding more participation, feeding more attitudes, and so on—can lead to employees becoming totally committed to achieving an injury-free workplace.

The *reciprocity* principle can fuel *The Participation Factor* by increasing actively caring behaviors and interdependency throughout a work culture. Specifically, when people go beyond the call of duty for the safety or health of another person, they induce a sense of obligation in that person to return the favor. They also set an example that spreads more actively caring through the principle of social *conformity*. Thus, when people actively care they activate two principles of social influence, which leads to more actively caring.

The principle of *authority* reminds us that people might follow orders blindly. We have learned from childhood to follow authority. This becomes a barrier to safety when a manager or supervisor asks a worker to perform a behavior that could endanger the worker, coworkers, or the environment. On the other hand, people in positions of authority can have the opposite effect. In fact, their role modeling and support of interdependency and actively caring is key to cultivating a Total Safety Culture.

Safety leaders should also remember the principle of *ingratiation* and use quality interpersonal recognition to a) support other people's participation for safety, b) increase other people's appreciation and respect for them, and c) increase their own admiration for those persons they recognize.

Finally, the social influence principle of *scarcity* explains why some employees actively resist complying with top-down safety rules, regulations, and quick-fix safety programs (referred to by many as "flavor-of-the-month"). Some work cultures seemingly restrict the perception of personal control and creativity when it comes to safety. And in these situations, noncompliance, nonparticipation, or "counter-participation" becomes a personal statement of "freedom." Employee involvement is much more likely with top-down support of safety processes that are developed, owned and continuously improved by work teams well educated to understand the rationale and relevancy of the principles behind their safety methods, procedures, and tools.

8

"A leader knows what's best to do; a manager knows merely how best to do it."

—Ken Adelman

The Essentials of Effective Leadership

Managers hold us accountable; leaders inspire us to be responsible and self-accountable. The Participation Factor in occupational safety needs both managers and leaders, but an injury-free workplace requires more leaders. Leaders are made—not born. We all have opportunities to lead participation for safety, but we don't always meet those opportunities with maximum effectiveness. This chapter shows you how to improve your leadership skills—from deciding when to instruct, support, coach, or delegate to leading change and building interpersonal trust throughout your work culture. A select few are assigned to manage, but we all have occasions to lead.

Initiating and maintaining participation in a safety improvement process requires substantial leadership. Leaders are needed to champion new principles and procedures and to keep effective interventions going. In fact, leadership makes the difference between a "flavor-of-the month" safety initiative and a long-term continuous improvement process. You can launch a process with excellent education and training, but you can't keep the momentum going without individuals who provide energy, enthusiasm, and the right example. This chapter covers some essentials of effective leadership.

I start with a discussion of the qualities of the most effective leaders, then consider one of the most significant determinants of participation that leaders influence markedly—interpersonal trust. Next, I cover the challenge of "change," including what we can expect when a change is proposed and how we can help people handle such change. Finally, I discuss three key strategies for getting more enthusiastic participation from everyone in an organization. These are basic techniques anyone can use to get people more "gung ho" about safety and thereby fuel *The Participation Factor.*

Qualities of Effective Leaders

First, we have to find the leaders. Who are they? The traditional definition of one person exerting influence over a group doesn't quite work for safety. Ask any safety manager who has been expected to do it all. To achieve and maintain an injury-free workplace, everyone needs to accept a leadership role in reducing injuries. Everyone needs to feel responsible for safety and go beyond their normal routines to protect others. This requires leadership skills.

Psychologists have studied leadership rigorously for over half a century in an attempt to define the traits and styles of good leaders (Yukl 1989). Still, many questions remain unanswered, making leadership more an art than a science. But several decades of research have turned up some important answers, which we'll now apply to safety.

Many psychologists consider the characteristics that distinguish leaders to be permanent and inborn personality traits (Kirkpatrick and Locke 1991), but I prefer to consider them response styles or personality states that can be taught and cultivated. If action plans or interventions can be developed to promote styles typical of the best leaders, then the number of effective safety leaders in an organization can be increased. The most effective leaders have all or most of the following qualities.

Passion

The most successful leaders show energy, desire, passion, enthusiasm, and constant ambition to achieve. Passion to achieve an injury-free workplace can be fueled by clarifying goals and tracking progress. Put a positive spin on safety and make it something to be achieved—not losses to be controlled. Then employees will be motivated to achieve shared safety goals just like they work toward production and quality goals. Marking progress leads to the genuine belief that the process works. This fires up employees to continue the process.

Honesty and Integrity

Effective leaders are open and trustworthy. An injury-free workplace depends on open interpersonal conversation. This obviously requires honesty, integrity, and trust. It's quite useful for work groups to discuss ways to nurture these qualities in their culture. Take a look at certain environmental conditions, policies, and behaviors. Some arouse suspicions of hidden agendas, politics, and selfish aims. In some cultures the scenario depicted on the next page is not that preposterous. You can work to eliminate some of these trust-busters by first identifying them, then discussing their purpose, and devising alternatives. Later in this chapter I explain more about the critical issue of interpersonal trust.

Some work cultures have low levels of interpersonal trust.

Compassion

Effective leaders show concern about the welfare of others. By showing compassion for their fellow employees, they set an active example for others to follow. They adopt the mindset that people are not numbers or interchangeable parts—they have feelings, concerns, and individual talents and attitudes that make them unique. When leaders operate from this perspective they enrich the working relationships of everyone they contact. They exemplify the kind of participation needed to sustain an injury-free workplace.

Motivation

Since most people really care about reducing personal injuries, even injuries to people they don't know, the motivation to lead others will spread naturally throughout a work culture when people believe they can have personal control over injuries. This occurs when they learn effective techniques to prevent injuries and feel empowered to apply them, as covered in Chapter 2.

Self-Confidence

Effective leaders trust in their own abilities to achieve (Baron 1995; Kirkpatrick and Locke 1991). Education helps convince people they can achieve, but they need ongoing support and recognition for their efforts. For example, the self-confidence needed to give safety-related feedback can be initiated with appropriate education and training, and can be maintained with coaching, communication, and recognition. Notice that enhancing three of the five empowerment factors discussed in Chapter 2—self-efficacy, personal control, and optimism—builds self-confidence.

Thinking Skills

Successful leaders can integrate large amounts of information, interpret it objectively and coherently, and act decisively as a result (Baron 1995; Kirkpatrick and Locke 1991). Constructive thinking skills evolve among team members when objective data are collected on the progress of safety interventions and are used to refine or expand these processes and develop new ones. This is basic scientific thinking, the key to substituting profound knowledge for common sense. This mindful learning (Langer 1997) and critical thinking lead to special expertise and to more constructive involvement. This is a primary aspect of behavior-based safety and key to its remarkable success at facilitating employee participation and reducing injury rates (Geller 2001d; Petersen 2001).

Expertise

To achieve and maintain an injury-free workplace, everyone needs to understand the principles behind policies, rules, and interventions to improve safety. When employees teach these principles to their coworkers, they develop the level of profound knowledge, expertise, and responsibility needed for exemplary leadership.

Flexibility

Successful leaders size up a situation and adjust their management style accordingly (Hersey and Blanchard 1982). Sometimes groups and circumstances call for firm direction—an autocratic style. At other times, the same people might work better under a nondirective, hands-off approach—a democratic style. The best leaders are good at assessing people and situations and then matching their approach to fit the need (Zaccaro, Foti, and Kenny 1991). Effective leaders size up the situation, especially the relative commitment and competence of the participants, and then direct, support, motivate, or delegate depending on this assessment (Blanchard, Zigarmi, and Zigarmi 1985).

Coaching Leadership. Figure 8.1 illustrates four leadership styles that depend on the amount of direction and motivation given (adapted from Blanchard 1999). Coaching typically involves a discussion of specific behaviors needed for a certain task as well as specific feedback to pinpoint effective and

Amount of Direction Employees Need

		Low	High
Amount of Motivation Employees Need	Low	Delegating	Instructing
	High	Supporting	Coaching

Figure 8.1 Four leadership styles are defined by the degree of direction and motivation employees need.

ineffective behaviors. In other words, coaches give direction according to an action plan and then follow up with appropriate support and correction. Periodic reminders keep people on the right track, while intermittent recognition provides motivation to keep people going.

Delegating Leadership. There are times when it's most appropriate for leaders to give an assignment in general terms (without specific direction) and to limit interpersonal behavior-focused feedback. The expectation is that team members are already motivated to do their best and will give each other direction, support, and feedback when needed. In other words, these individuals are personally accountable (responsible), and are expected to use self-management techniques (activators and consequences) to keep themselves motivated and on the right track (Geller 2001b).

Instructing Leadership. Some people are already highly motivated to perform well but don't know exactly what to do. This is often the case with new hires. They want to make a good first impression, and the newness of the job is naturally motivating. They are nervous, however, because of response uncertainty. They aren't sure what to do in a relatively novel situation. In this case, leaders need to focus on giving behavior-focused instruction.

This type of leadership should also be the approach at most athletic events. Individuals and teams in a sports contest do not typically need motivation. The situation itself, from fan support to peer pressure, often provides plenty of extrinsic motivation. What the competitors need are specific instructions for focusing their motivation. They need to know what specific behaviors are needed to win in various situations. Thus, the halftime speeches of team coaches should be more directional than motivational.

Supporting Leadership. Some people and situations require more support than direction. Take, for example, the experienced worker who does the same set of tasks day after day. This individual doesn't need direction, but could benefit from the periodic expression of sincere appreciation for a job well done.

There are times when experienced workers know what to do but don't perform up to par all of the time. This is not a training problem, but rather one of execution (Geller 2000a). Through proactive listening a leader can recognize this and provide the kind of support that increases motivation. This could involve broadening a job assignment, varying the task components, or assigning leadership responsibilities. But at least it should include the delivery of one-to-one recognition in ways that increase a person's sense of importance and self-worth, as detailed in Chapter 5.

Proactive Listening

So how can we know what type of safety leadership to use? That's where proactive observation and listening are critical. You need to observe others without premature bias about what you expect from them. Attributing certain abilities, attitudes or dispositions to others according to stereotypes (as illustrated below) will surely prevent the kind of assessment needed to deter-

Attributions based on stereotypes bias interpersonal assessment.

mine whether primarily a coaching, instructing, supporting, or delegating approach is needed. You need to make this assessment periodically for each situation and worker, given the dynamic characteristics of most work settings and the changing nature of people.

Consider, for example, the new employee who needs specific direction at first. Then, as he or she becomes familiar with the routine, more support than instruction is called for. Later, you decide to expand this individual's work assignment with no increase in financial compensation. This situation will probably benefit most from a coaching conversation in which both direction and support are given, at least at first. Eventually, a delegating approach might be most appropriate, where varying assignments are given with only outcome expectations. These workers are able to manage themselves with self-direction and self-motivation. But they still benefit from genuine words of appreciation when expectations are met.

The effective leaders of work teams change their management styles quite dramatically as group members become more familiar with each other and their mission. In the beginning, during the forming and storming stages of team progress (Tuckman 1965), work groups need structure, including specific direction and support. This implies a coaching or directing format. Later, when group members become familiar with each other's interests and talents and progress to the norming and performing stages of team development (Tuckman 1965; Tuckman and Jensen 1977), supporting or delegating leadership is needed.

An Illustrative Anecdote

Let me tell you about a most unusual and effective tennis lesson I observed that exemplifies the qualities of effective leadership reviewed here. Frank, my longtime tennis opponent, once had a strong forehand, but over the years it weakened considerably. It got so that I expected to win every set, and he expected the same. Eventually, he lost interest in our regular competition, and I lost a regular tennis opponent.

Then Josh Williams, a friend and associate at Safety Performance Solutions, stepped in to help. Josh played varsity tennis for four years at Kalamazoo College in Michigan and subsequently taught tennis professionally at John Newcome's tennis resort. When Josh arrived at our tennis court, I asked him if he wanted to watch Frank and me rally for a while so he could assess the problem. Numerous tennis instructors use this approach. They observe a client hit a tennis ball a number of times and then provide directive feedback by verbalizing and demonstrating certain behavioral changes. Then they observe some more and give more feedback.

I was surprised when Josh declined my assistance and instead took my side of the court and began rallying with Frank. He didn't say anything about any problem, just "Nice shot" a number of times to commend good performance.

At one point, Josh stopped rallying and asked Frank where he thought he was having difficulty. Convinced he knew his problem, Frank discussed the way he grips his racket when shifting from a backhand to a forehand stroke. Frank does hold his racket differently than most people do, using what's referred to as a Western Grip instead of the more common Eastern Grip.

Josh agreed with Frank's diagnosis and asked him to rally some more balls. This time Josh used the Western Grip that Frank used and mimicked his forehand stroke. In this way, Josh could understand exactly how it felt to be in Frank's tennis shoes. When switching from a backhand to a forehand stroke, Josh changed his grip exactly as Frank did in order to appreciate the difficulty Frank was experiencing.

With expertise, compassion, self-confidence, and honesty, Josh truly empathized with Frank's situation. As a result, he could provide relevant advice. Because Josh demonstrated genuine understanding and appreciation of Frank's problem, his advice was readily accepted. Thus, by observing and listening proactively, the effective leader shows both caring and credibility, and eventually makes the most valid recommendations for improvement. This process also builds a crucial ingredient for long-term participation—interpersonal trust.

The Critical Role of Interpersonal Trust

No human factor determines level of participation in a safety effort more than interpersonal trust. For example, behavior-based coaching for safety requires trust, not only between coworkers who apply an observation and feedback process to each other, but also between line workers and the managers who must support such a safety process (DePasquale and Geller 1999).

As I've already indicated, effective leaders are trustworthy and they engender trust among others. How do they do this? How can we increase this particular human dimension throughout a work force and thereby fuel *The Participation Factor*? This section offers some practical strategies for building interpersonal trust in a work culture. First let's explore the meaning of this concept and consider how to measure it.

What Is Interpersonal Trust?

The first definition of "trust" in my *American Heritage Dictionary* (1991) is "confidence in the integrity, ability, character, and truth of a person or thing" (p. 1300). "Interpersonal" merely limits this definition to "person" or situations between people. This definition refers to behavior ("ability") as well as internal or person-based dimensions ("integrity" and "character"). In other words, you could be confident a person means well, but you might doubt his or her ability to complete the intended task. In this case, you trust the individual's intentions, but you are not so sure the stated outcomes will occur. You lack confidence in the capability of the person to make good on his or her promises. This perception is common in situations where well-intentioned managers or safety leaders verbalize missions, goals, or policies that are viewed as idealistic or unrealistic. When punishment or reward contingencies are not carried out consistently and fairly, for example, people's interpersonal trust can be limited to intentions and not actions.

It's also possible for people to have faith in the ability of others, but to mistrust these individuals' intentions. This happens when employees are not kept informed of events or decisions leading up to a policy change that affects their work life. When a policy change is sprung on workers without warning or rationale, they might become suspicious of management's intentions. They might believe their leaders have the intellect and skills to make things happen, but be concerned about what particular things will happen. Do they really have our welfare in mind when they deliberate about changes in equipment design or production quotas?

Could there be a disconnection between intention and capability when management establishes a safety incentive program? Consider the incentive program that offers everyone a prize if no one gets hurt over a certain period of time. This translates into a contingency that puts pressure on individuals to cover up an injury. After all, if a person reports an injury, then everyone loses their reward. It's logical for workers to perceive this kind of program as a scheme to keep the numbers down without management really caring about their personal welfare. As discussed in Chapter 1, this type of program inhibits the very kinds of reports and interpersonal conversations needed for incident analysis and injury prevention.

Interpersonal Trust among Coworkers. All of the examples I've used so far to distinguish between trust in "intention" versus trust in "ability" refer to management. In other words, I focused on whether a worker has confidence in the intention and/or capability of a manager or supervisor. Interpersonal trust in a work culture also refers to the extent people ascribe good intentions and abilities to their peers. In other words, a line worker might have confidence in the ability of a coworker to perform a job safely and competently, but might be wary of telling him or her certain things because of a mistrust in that person's intentions. A coworker might think, for example, "My partner might use the information against me for personal gain—to get the promotion before me." Alternatively, you might trust the intentions of a coworker ("He would never take advantage of me"), but lack confidence in his capability on a particular job assignment ("I'm sure he will do his best, but I'm afraid his lack of experience means his best will not be good enough").

An Interpersonal Trust Scale. This discussion of interpersonal trust identified two dimensions of trust: a) faith in the *intentions* of others, and b) confidence in the *ability* of others. From the viewpoint of a line worker evaluating the overall interpersonal trust in a work culture, these dimensions can refer to two groups of people—coworkers and management. This fourfold classification system was used by Cook and Wall (1980) to derive the 12-item questionnaire shown in Figure 8.2. You can administer this scale to a discussion group or work team to stimulate interesting and instructive group discussion. It's an excellent way to increase people's understanding of interpersonal trust.

Ask the participants to score their own surveys as follows. Except for two items (2 and 12), the higher the scale value the greater the perceived interpersonal trust. Since items 2 and 12 are negatively phrased, these need to be reverse scored. In other words, for these two items, the number selected is first subtracted from 6, so a "1" becomes "5," a "2" becomes "4," and so on.

Totaling the 12 item scores (with items 2 and 12 reverse scored) yields an estimate of an individual's perception of overall interpersonal trust in his or her work culture. You can obtain an overall trust index by calculating the mean score from many respondents. You can also estimate the different dimensions of trust introduced here by referring to Figure 8.3. Specifically, items 1, 7, and 12 address faith in the intentions of management, while items 3, 5, and 8 assess faith in intentions of peers (coworkers). Confidence in the capability of management is assessed with items 2, 4, and 6, while the ability or actions of peers is measured by items 9, 10, and 11.

Please note that there is nothing special or magical about the wording of these items. You should feel free to reword a particular item if different language fits better with your culture. Plus, you could decide to add or substitute new items. Note also that the scale was developed to measure interpersonal trust from the viewpoint of an hourly worker. With only slight adjustments, the scale can also estimate interpersonal trust from a manager's perspective.

Building a Trusting Culture

Now that we have an operational definition of "interpersonal trust," the more important issue can be addressed: How can we increase interpersonal trust throughout a work culture? I searched the research literature for answers to this question and found none. Therefore, I attempted a common-sense approach. I called together a group of my research students and colleagues to discuss interpersonal trust. First I explained the concept of interpersonal trust, as defined here. Then I asked the question "How can we increase interpersonal

Figure 8.2 A survey to assess interpersonal trust (adapted from Cook & Wall 1980).

The statements below express opinions that people might hold about the confidence and trust that can be placed in others at work, both fellow workers and management. Circle the scale numbers next to each statement to indicate how much you agree with it. 1=Strongly Disagree (SD); 2=Disagree (D); 3=Not Sure (N); 4=Agree (A); 5=Strongly Agree (SA).

	SD	D	N	A	SA
1. Management is sincere in its attempts to understand the workers' point of view.	1	2	3	4	5
* 2. Our company has a poor future unless it can attract better managers.	1	2	3	4	5
3. If I got into difficulties at work I know my coworkers would try to help me out.	1	2	3	4	5
4. Management can be trusted to make sensible decisions for the company's future.	1	2	3	4	5
5. I can trust the people I work with to lend me a hand if I need it.	1	2	3	4	5
6. Management seems to do an effective job.	1	2	3	4	5
7. I feel quite confident that the company will always treat me fairly.	1	2	3	4	5
8. Most of my coworkers can be relied upon to do as they say they will.	1	2	3	4	5
9. I have full confidence in the skills of my coworkers.	1	2	3	4	5
10. Most of my fellow workers are able to do their work well even when supervisors are not around.	1	2	3	4	5
11. I can rely on other workers not to make my job more difficult by doing careless work.	1	2	3	4	5
*12. I would not be surprised if management tried to gain advantage by deceiving the workers.	1	2	3	4	5

* *When totaling your score, subtract the scale number for this item from 6.*

Figure 8.3 Fourfold classification of interpersonal trust with reference to the trust survey above.

	Management	**Coworkers**
Intention	Questions 1, 7, 12	Questions 3, 5, 8
Ability	Questions 2, 4, 6	Questions 9, 10, 11

trust among the members of our various research teams?" and facilitated a brainstorming discussion among these nine individuals. I wrote each suggestion on the blackboard and then attempted to assign an "intention" or "ability" label to each.

After arriving at a rather large list of comments related to the building of interpersonal trust, we refined our list with a consensus process. I asked for suggestions regarding the elimination or combination of list items. During this process we had to remind ourselves we were not looking for items that made us believe another person could be trusted in intention or ability. Rather, our assignment was to suggest ways for increasing perceptions of interpersonal trust.

After almost two hours, we arrived at an interesting and seemingly useful list of proposals for increasing interpersonal trust as well as a beneficial approach for teaching our recommendations to others. Before sharing our insights here, I need to make a very important point. This brainstorming process was extremely valuable. We not only arrived at a list of trust-building principles and procedures, we increased feelings of group cohesion and ownership around this critically important concept. We put the concept of interpersonal trust and the need to increase it on the table. We faced the reality that there are many things each of us can do to build interpersonal trust in our work culture. A summary of our brainstorming session is now posted in our meeting room, and we review it at the start of every semester (when new students join our research group).

I urge you to have a brainstorming session similar to the one we experienced. Your list of proposals will probably be similar to ours, but it will be owned by your group. This increases the likelihood people will heed the recommendations for increasing interpersonal trust. You might find it useful to use the following summary of our session as a kick-off for your meeting. You could ask for reactions to the key words that came from our discussion and make your own additions, substitutions, or refinements. Owning a set of recommendations for building interpersonal trust is an ideal first step toward encouraging trustworthy behavior and servicing *The Participation Factor*.

The Seven "C's" of Trust Building

Near the end of our two-hour brainstorming session on interpersonal trust, I asked the group if we could find certain words that would encapsulate our various suggestions for increasing trust. It seemed, in fact, that many words beginning with the letter "C" reflected specific recommendations for building interpersonal trust in a work culture. We reached a consensus on the seven C-words listed in Figure 8.4, which capture the essence of our group exercise. The phrases associated with these words summarize the key definitions given in both my *American Heritage* (1991) and *New Merriam-Webster* (1989) dictionaries.

THE SEVEN "C'S" OF TRUST BUILDING

1. **Communication**
   *Exchange of information or opinion
   by speech, writing, or signals*

2. **Caring**
   *Showing concern or interest
   about what happens*

3. **Candor**
   *Straightforwardness and frankness
   of expression; freedom from prejudice*

4. **Consistency**
   *Agreement among successive
   acts, ideas, or events*

5. **Commitment**
   *Being bound emotionally or intellectually
   to a course of action*

6. **Consensus**
   Agreement in opinion, testimony, or belief

7. **Character**
   *The combined moral or ethical structure
   of a person or group; integrity; fortitude*

Figure 8.4 Seven C-words define ways to enhance interpersonal trust.

Communication. This was the theme of Chapter 5. How we interact with others is obviously a key determinant of interpersonal trust. What people say and how they say it influences our trust in both their capability and their intentions. An individual's expertise is displayed by his or her spoken or written words and by the confidence and credibility linked to the words. I'm sure you've heard many times that the *way* something is said, including intonation, pace, facial expressions, hand gestures, and overall posture, has greater impact than what is actually said. And you've certainly experienced a change in your personal feelings of trust toward another person as the result of *how* that individual communicated information. Is it possible the high-tech electronic approaches to communication (like e-mail and phone messages) decrease face-to-face interaction and hence hamper the development of interpersonal trust? As illustrated below, without face-to-face conversations we can't verify the truth in some statements.

Caring. When you take the time to listen to another perspective, you send a most important message—you care. When people believe you sincerely care about them, they will care about what you tell them. They trust that you will look out for them when applying your knowledge, skills, and abilities. They trust your intention because they believe you care.

You also communicate caring and build interpersonal trust when you ask questions. I'm not talking about the probing questions we sometimes ask instead of actively listening. I'm referring to a question used to initiate conversation. And I'm not talking about the typical general questions we often ask people we haven't seen for a while. "How are you doing?" we ask, and we get the standard reply: "I'm doing fine, how about you?" No, I'm referring to inquiry about a particular task or set of circumstances: "That's a unique way to clean the equipment. Why do you do it that way?" Questions targeting a specific aspect of a person's job send the signal you care about him or her.

Telephone conversations allow for distortion of personal disposition.

This communication is more than a general greeting. It's a statement of genuine interest in what people are doing and how they feel. It's especially powerful when your words reflect your concern about health and safety.

In order to show caring with specific behavior-based questions, you need to take the time to learn what others are doing. This comes from active listening and behavior-based observation. I'm sure you have heard the phrase "Walk the talk." Well, here I'm talking about "listening to the talk and watching the walk." This shows you care and gives you an opportunity to "talk the walk" so people will trust your intentions.

Candor. We trust people who are frank and open with us. They don't beat around the bush. They get right to the point, whether asking for a favor or giving us feedback about our participation. When these individuals don't know an answer to our questions they don't ignore us or hem or haw about possibilities. They tell us outright when they don't know something, and they tell us they'll get back to us later. When they get back to us soon with an answer, our trust in both their intention and ability increases.

The second dictionary definition of "candor"—freedom from prejudice—reflects another important aspect of trust building. When a person's interactions with you reflect prejudice or the tendency to evaluate or judge another person on the basis of a stereotype or preconceived notion about group characteristics, you have reason to mistrust this individual. You are rightfully suspicious about this person's ability to evaluate others and his or her intention to treat people fairly. Even when the prejudice is not directed at you, your trust in this person decreases. Right?

When someone gives an opinion about another person based on race, religion, gender, age, sexual orientation, or birthplace, you should doubt this person's ability to make people-related decisions. You should wonder whether this person's intention to perform on behalf of another person will be biased or tainted by a tendency to prejudge others on the basis of overly simple and usually inaccurate stereotypes.

Consistency. We usually trust the intentions of people who confess openly their inability to answer our questions. Our trust in them might increase when they tell us they'll get back to us right away with a response. But what happens when we must wait a long time for a reply? Or suppose we never hear from them again? Now what happens to interpersonal trust? Obviously, I'm talking about consistency, a word everyone in our discussion group mentioned as a determinant of interpersonal trust. I'm sure you recall that consistency was one of the social influence principles discussed in Chapter 7.

Perhaps the quickest way to destroy interpersonal trust is to not follow through consistently with our agreements. A promise is essentially a behavior-consequence contingency. It specifies that a certain consequence will follow a certain behavior. Whether the consequence is positive or negative, trust decreases when the behavior is not rewarded or punished as promised.

One of the problems with punishment contingencies is that they are difficult to implement fairly and consistently. It's easy to state a policy that anyone not using appropriate personal protective equipment will be "written up," but it's quite difficult or impossible to carry out this contingency consistently. What about safety incentive programs that offer everyone a reward when no injuries occur over a designated time period and participants see coworkers get hurt but don't turn in injury reports? Similar trust-busting effects occur with "safe employee of the month" programs that select winners according to nonobjective criteria or that don't consider everyone consistently as potential award recipients.

Commitment. People who are dependable and reliable are not only showing consistency, they are demonstrating commitment. When you follow through on a promise or pledge to do something, you tell others they can count on you. You can be trusted to do what you say you will do. Making a commitment and honoring it builds trust in both intention and ability.

In Chapters 1 and 4, I conveyed the need to get people talking about their personal safety-related experiences, from their near hits and injuries to firsthand observations of protection from a safety device. The rationale I gave was that personal stories are motivational and memorable because audiences can visualize themselves in the same situation. Here I want to add that telling a personal anecdote to illustrate a point demonstrates commitment and increases credibility. The audience has reason to trust your intention to give accurate and useful information.

Whenever I give presentations on the psychology of safety, I try to work in one or more personal experiences. I've done many things over the years in an attempt to promote safety, and when a story fits the theme of my talk, the audience hears firsthand evidence of my commitment. When I discuss the value of using safety belts, for example, I can relate any of a number of interventions I've tried over the years to encourage people to buckle up—from setting up safety-belt incentive programs at numerous industrial and community sites to teaching my young daughters to hold up a "Please Buckle Up —I Care" flash card whenever we stopped at an intersection.

Consensus. Demonstrating personal commitment to a mission, purpose, or goal helps to build group consensus. When a group of people reach consensus about something, all group members agree on a decision or course of action and are willing to support it. Leaders or group facilitators who develop consensus among people build interpersonal trust. Consensus building is the opposite of top-down decision making, and is not the same as negotiating, calling for a vote and letting the majority win, or working out a compromise between two differing sets of opinions.

Whenever the result of a group decision-making process comes across as "win-lose," some mistrust is going to develop. A majority of the group might be pleased, but others will be discontented and might actively or passively resist involvement. Even the "winners" could feel reduced interpersonal trust. "We won *this* decision, but what about next time?" Without solid support for the decision, the outcome will be less than desired. Without everyone's buy-in and commitment, we can't expect optimal participation.

I offer guidelines for consensus building elsewhere (Geller 2001c); see also Rees (1997). Here I want to convince you of the value of building consensus on a group process or action plan. You also need to realize consensus-building is not easy. There's no quick fix to arriving at consensus. It requires plenty of interpersonal communication, including straightforward opinion sharing, intense discussion, emotional debate, active listening, careful evaluation, methodical organization, and systematic prioritizing. But on important matters, the outcome is well worth the investment. When you develop a solution or process every potential participant can get behind and champion, you have cultivated the degree of interpersonal trust needed for total involvement.

Character. This final C-word means different things to different people. Generally, a person with "character" is considered honest, ethical, and principled. People with character are credible or worthy of another person's trust because they display confidence and competence in following a consistent set of morally sound beliefs. They are believable and trusted because they know who they are; they know where they want to go; and they know how to get there.

All of the strategies discussed here for cultivating a trusting culture are practiced by a person with character. Therefore, this C-word epitomizes interpersonal trust from both the intention and ability perspective. I'd like to add a few additional trust-building methods that also fit this category, although they naturally overlap with other C-words discussed here.

First, individuals with character are willing to admit *vulnerability*. They realize they aren't perfect and need behavioral feedback from others. To improve, they may ask others, "On a scale of 1 to 10, how safe are my work practices?" They know their strengths and weaknesses, and find exemplars to model.

By actively listening to others and observing their behaviors, individuals with character learn how to improve their own performance. If they're building a high-performance team, they can readily find people with knowledge, skills, and abilities to complement their own competencies. They know how to make diversity work for them, their group, and the entire organization. They understand the important lesson illustrated below, namely that group decision-making and participation benefit from diversity, even though obtaining consensus from a diverse group is relatively cumbersome and time consuming.

Having the courage to admit your weaknesses means you're *willing to apologize* when you've made a mistake and *willing to ask for forgiveness*. There is probably no better way to build trust between individuals than for one person to own up to an error that might have affected the other person. Of course you should also indicate what you will do better next time, or you should ask for specific advice on how to improve. This kind of vulnerability enables you to heed the powerful enrichment principle I learned from Frank Bird and George Germain (1987)—"Good, better, best. Never let us rest, until good is better, and better best" (p. 111).

What is your trust level for a group leader who not only admits failure but continually seeks ways to improve? This is the kind of person you want on your team. Right! You can level with this person about your own incompe-

Diversity benefits group decision-making and participation.

tencies or insecurities without fear of ridicule or reprisal. You trust this person will appreciate your desire to improve and will offer the guidance you need to do better. You also trust this individual to maintain the confidentiality of any disclosure of personal failure or vulnerability.

While admitting personal vulnerability is a powerful way to build interpersonal trust, the surest way to *reduce* interpersonal trust is to tell one person about the weakness of another. In this situation it's natural to think, "If he talks that way about her, I wonder what he says about me behind my back." It's obvious how criticizing or demeaning others in their absence can lead to interpersonal suspicion and mistrust.

Back-stabbing leads to more back-stabbing and eventually to a work culture of independent people doing their own thing, fearful of making an error and unreceptive to any kind interpersonal observation and feedback. Participation won't improve or increase in such a culture. Start to build interpersonal trust by making a personal commitment and implementing a team policy of "No back-stabbing." People with character, as defined here, always talk about other people as if the other people can hear them. In other words, to replace interpersonal mistrust with trust, never criticize other individuals behind their backs.

Summary

The fourfold classification system for interpersonal trust is an important contribution of the Cook and Wall survey tool. In industrial settings, it's instructive to differentiate perceptions of interpersonal trust as targeting management or coworkers and with regard to another person's intentions or actions.

The research literature offers limited guidance on how to build interpersonal trust throughout a work culture. Therefore, it's necessary at this point to resort to common sense or to what people conclude from personal experience. The most frequent recommendation I've heard from consultants and practitioners regarding the facilitation of interpersonal trust is to be trustworthy. "If you want others to trust you," they say, "you need to trust others and behave toward others in ways that warrant their trust." This is certainly sound advice, but a critical question remains: "What kinds of behaviors are trustworthy?"

The seven C-words reviewed here are easy to remember, and although their meanings overlap to some extent, each offers distinct directives for trust-building. *Communicating* these guidelines to others in a *candid* and *caring* way opens up the kind of dialogue that starts people on a journey of interpersonal trust-building. Then people need to give each other *consistent* and *candid* feedback about behavior related to these trust-building principles.

With *character* and *commitment*, we need to recognize others for participation that cultivates interpersonal trust, and offer corrective feedback when there's room for improvement. And the recipients of such feedback need to accept it with *caring* appreciation and a *commitment* to improve. Then feedback recipients need to show the *character* to thank the observer for the feedback, even when the *communication* is not all positive and is not delivered well. They might offer feedback on how to make the feedback more useful. Dialogue like this is necessary to build *consensus* and sustain a journey of continuous trust-building. Such a journey fuels *The Participation Factor* and enables the achievement of an injury-free workplace.

Leading Change

Change occurs all of the time. In fact, it's fair to say that change is a constant. We usually don't even notice change, however, unless it affects us. Sometimes the change we notice is inconsequential, but sometimes it includes consequences that impact us directly and severely. For example, the boys illustrated below don't recognize a significant change in their school day, and dire consequences are likely if they don't adjust to the change. Often we are called upon to do more than adjust to change, however. We are asked to participate

Not anticipating change can lead to dire consequences.

in the change process. This is viewed as positive if we see the change as good for us, but can be quite uncomfortable if we believe the change will affect us negatively.

I've heard insanity defined as "continuing to do the same thing day after day and expecting improvement." This implies, of course, that improvement requires change. In fact, improvement *is* change. Nevertheless, people often resist change in their job settings. They are secure and in control in their "comfort zones," and can feel threatened by a presumed loss of control or predictability following a proposed change in their work assignment, environment, or culture. Effective leaders sell people on beneficial change and inspire them to participate actively in facilitating a change process. In this section I offer guidelines for doing this.

Levels of Participation

Before addressing ways to get people involved in a change process, let's consider levels of participation. I believe there are essentially five:

- *Level 1*—the leaders or innovators who are totally involved

- *Level 2*—those who want to participate but need a little direction and support

- *Level 3*—those, usually the majority, who are neutral or nervous about the change and need prodding and encouragement from others

- *Level 4*—the passive resisters who are critical and untrusting of something new imposed on them and use apathy and cynicism as excuses to remain uninvolved

- *Level 5*—the active resisters who view change as a threat or a loss of personal control and might exert measures to stifle the participation of others

A key point is that the active resisters stick out and attract attention. Non-participants use them to rationalize their own commitment to stay in their comfort zones. Managers aim their attention at these individuals, sometimes with the administration of punitive measures. This only builds resentment of the system among all resisters and makes it less likely they will join the change process. For some, such disciplinary attention does nothing but fuel their desire to exert independence and resist control, leading to vigorous recruitment of others to oppose the change.

Leaders need to focus their attention on the participants rather than the nonparticipants. If possible, active and passive resisters should be ignored. Recognize and support those willing to try the new process. Encourage those totally involved in the process (Level 1) to help people who believe in the change but are not yet totally immersed (Level 2). Then these two groups can work with the majority (Level 3) who need direction, support, and examples to follow.

When the change becomes the norm, the passive resisters (Level 4) will feel the peer pressure and fall in line. Some active resisters (Level 5) may never participate, but at least they will become passive and harmless to the status quo.

Levels of Buy-In

People are certainly not confined to a certain participation level, and their assigned participation level is neither exclusive nor fixed. They could be wavering between any two levels, ready to move up or down the participation hierarchy. Which direction they move depends on their commitment or level of buy-in for a particular level of participation.

The letters A, B, and C are useful for identifying three levels of people's acceptance of change and willingness to participate in a change process. First, people must become *aware* of the change, including a rationale for the change. Success in convincing people that a change is useful and worth the effort results in a shift in their *belief*, particularly the key empowerment beliefs introduced in Chapter 2—self-efficacy, response-efficacy, and outcome-expectancy. However, people might believe in the benefits of a particular change process but still not participate completely. The "C" level is *commitment*, which implies total involvement in the change process.

Two other "C" words, *choice* and *control*, suggest ways to go from awareness and belief to commitment. As I discussed in Chapters 2 and 4, when people are given choice throughout the development and implementation of a change process, they increase their perceptions of personal control and thus their commitment to contribute to the change.

The six letters of the word "change" can represent words that signify particular strategies for facilitating awareness, belief, and eventually commitment to participate in a given change process. That is, the word "change" can be used as a mnemonic for remembering the dimensions to consider when leading a change such as the initiation of a new safety process. Each word suggests questions to resolve in order to move people from awareness to commitment and participation.

"C" for Consequences

Let's face it; everyone plays this radio station: WIIFM—What's In It For Me? Change implies uncertainty, meaning people aren't sure what the consequences will be for them. Maintaining a familiar routine can seem more pleasant because the inputs and outputs are certain—no surprises.

So it's important to clarify the benefits and costs (positive and negative consequences) of a new program or process. Don't let people speculate on

C onsequences

H abit

A ttitude

N eeds

G oal setting

E mpowerment

Figure 8.5 The letters of CHANGE suggest strategies for leading change.

how a particular change will affect them. Be forthright about the extra effort or adjustment involved in making the change work, and emphasize the positive consequences that can be expected. Focus on the potential and probable benefits that will be added to the workplace as a result of the change. If you can't define additional positive consequences to gain and/or negative consequences to avoid with the new or added process, you'll have a difficult time motivating participation. I'm talking about providing outcome-expectancies, as entertained in Chapter 2.

Sometimes the change process appears overwhelming, and the benefits of the proposed change are not certain or immediate enough to motivate participation. This is especially the case for safety initiatives that seemingly detract from the more certain and immediate consequences of competing activities like production. In this case, it's useful to show that the change is less overwhelming and intrusive than it might seem. Or, you may have overlooked some positive consequences, other than the delayed bottom line of injury reduction, that could motivate buy-in and involvement. The next five words suggest strategies for addressing these issues.

"H" for Habit

Proactive change usually requires a change in behavior. Whether working on a new machine or implementing a new procedure, we alter our way of doing things. This means we need to eliminate old habits as well as develop new ones. When our daily routine is changed even slightly, new behaviors are substituted for old ones. Of course, we can adjust our behavior only through feedback, and often the necessary feedback is not automatically available. Therefore, some proactive change requires an ongoing feedback process to help people make the necessary adjustments in their behavior.

Remember that old habits are often difficult to break. Fold your hands, for example, and note which thumb is on top—left or right. Now fold your hands with the opposite thumb on top. Does this seem awkward? Now fold your arms in front of you, in the habitual way you've done it for years. Try reversing which arm is on top, and again notice how unusual it feels to perform a simple behavior like this in a new way. Of course, if you continue to reverse how you fold your hands or your arms, you will accommodate. With practice the new behavior will feel natural. In time, a new habit will be formed.

So don't expect people to demonstrate appropriate behavior change right away, even if everyone expresses buy-in and commitment up front. Sometimes old habits need to be broken. Patience is indeed a virtue as is an ongoing feedback process.

"A" for Attitude

People can develop a negative attitude about a change initiative by the very manner in which it is presented. If the change comes across as top-down and dictatorial, some people might "go negative" to assert their individual freedom. "I might do what you want, but I don't have to like it. You can't control my attitude."

Opinions about a new safety initiative might be negative at first, but you can facilitate positive attitudes by allowing people choice and a sense of personal control throughout the change process. You also boost acceptance and potential participation when you address people's needs.

"N" for Needs

You assure buy-in and facilitate commitment if you show people their needs are being addressed during the transformation process, and that although the change might be uncomfortable and inconvenient at first, the eventual outcome will be positive on a "need satisfaction scale." In other words, the change can be justified in terms of people's needs.

It's easy to justify safety initiatives in terms of need satisfaction. However, it's important to contrast short-term versus long-term needs. Teach people to look beyond their personal and immediate needs and consider the long-term group needs addressed by a proactive change for occupational safety. In other words, a collective and long-term view clarifies the need for an effective safety process.

"G" for Goal Setting

Goal setting turns a vision for proactive change into action. Remember, though, goals must be specific, motivational, attainable, relevant, and trackable (and the first letters of these words spell SMART, as I discussed in Chapter 5). Your vision for an injury-free environment, for example, can't be realized without defining proactive process goals that track relevant progress toward achieving this vision. This is how you document incremental change leading eventually to the major change defined by your vision. By defining the human needs to be satisfied after achieving successive goals, you'll motivate involvement in the change process.

"E" for Empowerment

As I detailed in Chapter 2, people feel empowered to participate in a change process when they have the knowledge and resources to achieve SMART goals, feel a sense of self-efficacy and personal control over the change process, and expect success from their change efforts. Certain steps can be taken to increase these perceptions. To find out what they are, ask potential participants, "What would increase your belief that this change initiative is not only within your domain of personal control, but that the effect will be worth the effort?"

If you respond to participants' reactions to this question in ways that convince them they have the necessary information, resources, and ability to accomplish SMART goals in a change initiative, the participants will expect the best and feel empowered to make the change happen. Then you will have been effective at leading change. Now let's consider three primary ways to get everyone more gung ho about participating for safety.

Three Key Leadership Principles

While attending a seminar by Dr. Kenneth Blanchard, co-author of the classic best seller *The One-Minute Manager,* I discovered that in 1998 he had written a book with Sheldon Bowles that applies directly to our discussions here on leadership and *The Participation Factor.* The title of the book says it all—*Gung Ho! Turn On the People in Any Organization* (Blanchard and Bowles 1998). This book reveals three basic "secrets" for getting more enthusiastic employee involvement.

I want to teach you these three secrets as they relate to increasing participation in safety-related efforts. This information won't be new to readers of *The Participation Factor*, but the creative way that Drs. Blanchard and Bowles state the obvious is invaluable. Learning these three secrets can improve your ability to teach basic philosophies you already know but perhaps don't use enough. With these basic principles, we can all become safety leaders and increase people's quality involvement in efforts to reduce workplace injuries.

Secret 1: The Spirit of the Squirrel

This secret is revealed by watching squirrels scurrying about collecting and storing food. They work with high energy because they're motivated, and they're motivated because their work is critical. If they don't store enough food for the winter, they will starve. So the "Spirit of the Squirrel" is *worthwhile work*.

If you convince employees their work is worthwhile, they'll be more motivated to participate. How do you do this? Help people see the bigger picture beyond their daily work routine. A bricklayer, for example, could describe his job as "laying brick" or as "building a community recreation center to bring people together for healthy recreation and exercise." Both descriptions are accurate, but you know which one sounds more worthwhile and stimulating.

Similarly, a work crew washing windows at a restaurant could consider their job as only washing windows or as providing clear vision for customers. Dishwashers in a university cafeteria might think they are merely cleaning food from dishes, but they are really assuring that students don't get sick from bacteria. Perhaps a car mechanic believes he is simply repairing a vehicle,

The Spirit of the Squirrel is worthwhile work.

194

but really he's making it possible for a family to travel safely from one important destination to another. And the receptionist is not merely answering telephones, rather she is an ambassador for her company. She is the "Executive Director of First Impressions."

Bottom line: Effective leaders help people see the bigger picture regarding their jobs. Whatever their profession, they're making a difference. They're helping to make the world a better place.

Safety and the Spirit of the Squirrel. Safety professionals naturally have the Spirit of the Squirrel. Safety work is obviously worthwhile. You care for everyone's primary asset—their safety and health. The challenge is to convince people the routine safety-related activities, from wearing uncomfortable protective equipment to conducting periodic environmental and behavioral audits, are really worthwhile.

As I explained back in Chapter 1, personal testimony is more effective than company statistics at getting this point across. When employees can visualize injuries prevented by their involvement, they can see how their safety work makes a difference. Like the squirrel's work, their safety-related participation helps colleagues and friends make it through the winter and beyond.

Heroes at Every Role. This principle relates directly to the conclusions from a 25-year survey conducted by the Gallup Organization (Buckingham and Coffman 1999). One million employees within 2500 business units across 24 companies were asked more than 100 questions related to effective leadership. The analysis of results revealed a key leadership principle—help people find the job most suited to their talents and interests, and when the right fit is found, do whatever it takes to maintain that participation. In other words, create heroes at every job by recognizing people's strengths and convincing them their particular job is worthwhile. When people achieve self-efficacy, personal control, and optimism at a particular task, leaders need to support that participation by remembering the Spirit of the Squirrel and applying quality recognition, as detailed in Chapter 5.

The Peter Principle. A common myth in business is detrimental to sustaining the most talented participation for each job and optimizing the system. Specifically, management seems to believe that promotion is the best way to reward excellence. That is, when employees excel at their jobs, it's common to offer them promotions to other jobs with higher salaries and more authority.

The best rewards are not typically available for doing what talented workers do best, but rather for taking on different jobs, often at other locations. Moving up in the business world typically means leaving a job you do well. Thus, work systems are periodically disrupted while a new employee attempts to fill the shoes of a worker who developed special talents for the job but has been promoted to another. With continued promotions, people can end up in a job at which they are relatively incompetent. This phenomenon has been termed the "Peter Principle" (Peter 1969).

A ramification of this large-scale problem is illustrated below. As silly as the manager's statement sounds, it's not that far-fetched. Have you ever accepted a promotion to another job because staying at the same position would imply failure or perhaps just resistance to reaching your potential? Or, have you ever considered another person somewhat less than successful because he or she has been at the same job for so many years?

When I tell people I've been a faculty member at the same university for more than thirty years, I sometimes sense a need to explain that I have received a number of offers to leave Virginia Tech. Why do I feel this way? Yes, this unfortunate and widespread myth that the most competent workers get successively promoted to new positions affects us all. We all need to convince ourselves and others that the work we are talented at is worthwhile. Then we need to find ways to promote employees to a higher status level by doing the *same* job rather than leaving for another. One sure way to do this is to empower

It can be detrimental to stay at the same job too long.

people to add challenging participation in safety-related activities to their routine job assignments.

Secret 2: The Way of the Beaver

A squirrel's behavior is fluent, filled with purposeful energy, but it can be rather chaotic and noncooperative. In fact, if you watch squirrels long enough, you're bound to see some win/lose conflict. Two squirrels might fight over a single acorn, and acorns buried by one squirrel for the winter will be another squirrel's treasure if they are found. Squirrels work hard—but they do so independently.

Beavers work *interdependently*. They have the Spirit of the Squirrel, but as the more intelligent rodent, they cooperate to get the job done. The beavers in a working colony seem to have their own job assignments. They "work like beavers" to complete various important tasks. Some collect and store twigs and sticks for winter food, others gnaw down trees for dams, others drag or float lumber to the site of a dam, others dig canals for floating logs long distances, and still others plug spaces between dam logs with stones and mud.

The Way of the Beaver is win/win interdependency.

When one beaver senses a predator, it slaps its tail hard on the surface of the water to make a loud noise and warn the others.

Blanchard (1999) emphasizes there is no "boss beaver." Watch beavers work—there's no way of determining who's in charge. The Way of the Beaver means being self-directed to achieve goals that benefit everyone. It means defining each worker's domain of influence as it relates to specific shared goals, and then letting each individual take control of his or her job. Employees are not expected to leave their brains at home, but instead are in charge of their particular domains of responsibility.

Effective leaders facilitate this "secret" by initiating a process or action plan with expectations rather than mandates. What's the difference? Both approaches specify desirable outcomes and establish the need for certain behaviors or process participation. However, expectations imply choice. While a certain outcome is anticipated, there is room for individual and group decision-making regarding procedures and methods. When people realize what's expected of them but perceive that they have some personal control in how to reach specific goals, they are more likely to own the process and make the transition from an other-directed to a self-directed mindset.

This principle exemplifies empowerment as I described in Chapter 2. Workers who feel empowered believe they can make a difference and are more likely to actively participate for the safety and health of others. Remember, research has linked five mental states or beliefs to perceptions of empowerment: self-efficacy ("I can do it"), response-efficacy ("My job is relevant"), outcome-expectancy ("My job produces worthwhile results), personal control ("I'm in control"), and optimism ("I expect the best").

The Way of the Beaver reflects these five states. Beavers know their various jobs (self-efficacy) and realize they're important (response-efficacy) in attaining significant consequences (outcome-expectancy). They're in control of achieving individual goals that benefit the group. And they're optimistic about reaching their goals—just observe how eagerly each beaver works.

Secret 3: The Gift of the Goose

Geese epitomize interdependency. Just look at them in flight. They form a "V," with a leader up front and each following goose flying in the draft created by the one immediately in front. The lead goose eventually tires of the headwind and moves back in the "V," replaced by another goose. This is true interdependence.

There's something else about geese in flight—that honking sound. Which geese are honking? It's all of them. Each one frequently honks, as though they are cheering each other on. That's the "Gift of the Goose." Geese provide each other with constant verbal support, recognizing how each member of the fly-

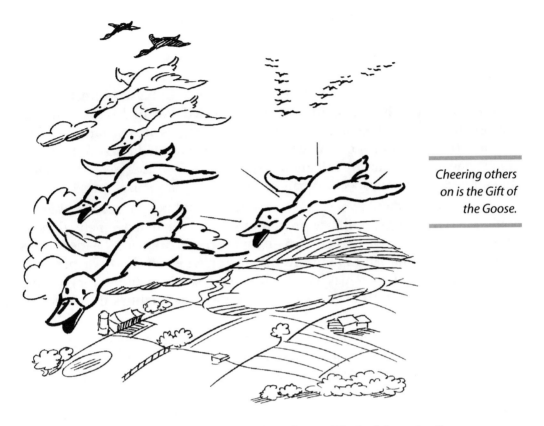

Cheering others on is the Gift of the Goose.

ing team allows the group to make headway. Their "cheering" encourages continued cooperation.

Recognizing and encouraging positive behaviors that make a difference reflects the remarkable power of positive reinforcement (Daniels 2000; Geller 1996, 2001d). This is a key principle of increasing and sustaining quality participation.

When work cultures display as much teamwork and cheerleading for safety-related participation as reflected in a flock of geese, exemplary levels of safety performance are attained. Don't forget, though, you need something to cheer about. Establish safety process activities that involve employees working interdependently to reduce environmental hazards and at-risk behaviors. Then injuries will surely be prevented. Let the honking begin!

In Conclusion

The terms "management" and "leadership" are used interchangeably, but these words reflect different job assignments and responsibilities. Both are necessary to achieve the quantity and quality of participation needed to achieve and maintain an injury-free workplace. Simply put, managers hold people accountable for doing something, whereas leaders inspire people to *want* to do something. In other words, managers provoke other-directed participation, while leaders influence self-persuasion and self-directed participation.

Although it's usually more desirable for people to be self-directed than other-directed, much participation is other-directed. We all do certain things because of an external accountability system. Managers are in charge of these systems; that's part of their job description. They are held accountable for monitoring a performance evaluation system that holds other people accountable for accomplishing specific goals or reaching certain milestones.

Safety management is necessary at times to hold people accountable for doing the right things for injury prevention. However, management alone is not sufficient to achieve and sustain an injury-free workplace. Leadership is needed to build the kind of culture that inspires responsibility or personal accountability for safety. This chapter reviewed essential qualities for effective leadership as well as strategies for developing these qualities throughout a work culture.

Research has shown that the most effective leaders display passion, integrity, compassion, empathy, motivation, self-confidence, thinking skills, expertise, and flexibility. These are not inborn traits, but are dynamic states that can be benefited or impaired by a work culture. Regarding flexibility, effective leaders observe and listen attentively in order to decide which of four basic kinds of leadership is called for—instructing, supporting, delegating, or coaching.

Effective leaders understand the role of competence and commitment in ascertaining the kind of leadership needed in a particular situation. When competence is high, people know what to do and therefore don't need direction. They might need supportive leadership, however, if their commitment is low.

Coaching leadership is needed when both a person's competence and commitment with regard to a particular task are low. In this case, leaders provide specific direction and feedback to improve competence. They increase commitment by delivering the kind of quality recognition described in Chapter 5. When leaders observe that people know what to do (competence) and are motivated to do it (commitment), they delegate.

How do you know when an individual or work team is ready for delegating leadership? Why not ask them. If they indicate they're not ready for delegation, then ask them what they need to reach this level of competence and commitment. Please realize, however, that even at the delegating stage, people appreciate genuine recognition for their participation. Note also that relying on interpersonal conversation to diagnose the type of leadership needed requires interpersonal trust.

Effective leaders do as much as possible to build interpersonal trust throughout their work culture. No other factor is more important than trust in increasing the kind of interpersonal participation needed to achieve an injury-free workplace. Lack of trust inhibits the cultivation of belonging and interdependency and prevents interpersonal responsibility for occupational safety.

The twelve-item survey reproduced in this chapter can be used to assess levels of trust in your work culture and teach a fourfold classification scheme for defining interpersonal trust. Specifically, trust can be about people's intentions, independent of their ability, and vice versa. Also, an interpersonal trust index can target either management or line workers.

Seven C-words were discussed with regard to building trust, namely *communication, caring, candor, consistency, commitment, consensus,* and *character*. The first three words relate directly to the support of safety conversations, covered in Chapter 5, while the next three reflect the social influence principle of consistency and conformity, discussed in Chapter 7. And the last C-word —character—epitomizes the essence of this chapter, namely the special qualities of effective leaders.

Effective leaders help people accept change and inspire them to participate in a change process. They watch for people who display immediate interest and commitment, and that's where they focus their attention—on the innovators who have dramatic positive influence on the rest of the work force. They give these folks all the education and skills training they need.

What about the resisters? Leaders essentially leave them alone. They don't give these individuals opportunities to dig in and become more committed to their contrary opinions. Instead, they give them opportunities to receive training and participate in the new process when they decide it's worth their effort.

Effective leaders realize that six issues need to be addressed when attempting to get people to buy in to change. These are readily remembered by referring to the letters in the word "change." First, address the *consequences* (advantages and disadvantages) of changing versus not changing. Then, consider the *habits* (or behaviors) that need to be adjusted, and the *attitude* we want to associate with the process. Involvement is motivated by pointing out the long-term individual and group *needs* satisfied by the change, and by using appropriate *goal-setting* procedures to translate a general vision into specific action plans. Finally, if the participants perceive they have the necessary information, resources, ability, and personal control to accomplish a goal they believe will bring worthwhile outcomes, they will expect the best and feel *empowered* to make the change happen.

This chapter ended with a discussion of three fundamental approaches for fueling *The Participation Factor*. Leaders can apply these so-called "secrets" (Blanchard and Bowles 1998) on a daily basis to increase people's involvement in any ongoing process. Specifically, follow the "Spirit of the Squirrel" and convince people their work is worthwhile. They will feel important, a key empowerment strategy taught by Dale Carnegie (1936) and his followers.

"The Way of the Beaver" reflects a theme this book introduced back in Chapter 1—the need to move from a dependent or independent mindset toward occupational safety to a state of interdependency. Such a transformation cannot happen overnight, but the ultimate work climate can be reached by cultivating the qualities of effective leaders throughout an organization and building interpersonal trust, belonging, and mutual commitment.

Along your journey of continuous improvement, don't forget the third secret—"The Gift of the Goose." Recognize individuals and groups appropriately and frequently to support the type of participation that contributes to achieving an interdependent culture of people actively caring for the safety and health of others. This is the most direct route to attaining and sustaining an injury-free workplace.

From Principles to Applications: Thirty Ways to Fuel *The Participation Factor*

The first eight chapters of this book address the human dynamics of safety with a distinct focus—the challenge of getting more people involved in injury prevention. The concepts and principles are founded on research, and are applicable in various situations for a multitude of missions. For example, the concept of self-efficacy alone has been used in every domain where people's attitudes or behaviors can have relevant impact—from one-on-one counseling in a therapist's office to group development of peak performance among athletes, teachers, and community change agents. However, I find no field in greater need of the appropriate attention to this and other basic psychological principles than occupational safety.

I sincerely hope this presentation of principles and practical strategies for fueling *The Participation Factor* in occupational safety will serve the following functions:

- Provide you with new action plans or interventions to implement.
- Provide you with a rationale to support what you already do to increase the quality and quantity of employee participation in safety-related activities.
- Provide you with realistic ideas for refining things you currently do for occupational safety in order to attract more participation and provoke less resistance.

Given these three pragmatic objectives, I couldn't end this book without listing a number of straightforward strategies applicable in almost any setting to benefit participation. Hence the need for this summary chapter. There's nothing new in this list of thirty ways to energize *The Participation Factor*. They all come directly from the lessons already covered. As such, this chapter merely reviews the book. You might find this listing useful, however, when deciding what action plan you and your coworkers can implement now to begin improving the human dynamics of safety at your work site.

This list of summary points is not exhaustive. It includes only a select number of action items inferable from the eight preceding chapters. I hope you will derive more. This is only a start. There is nothing special about the order. Actually, I hope you will derive your own priority list from these thirty recommendations and do something immediately to fuel *The Participation Factor* for safety at your work site.

The easiest thing you can do is probably the most important. You can teach others the concepts and methods presented here for enhancing involvement in occupational safety. Then you will have a team of individuals who can select a number of action items from the following list and beyond to fuel *The Participation Factor* for safety at your work site.

1. Watch Your Language

This was a primary theme in Chapter 5, and is perhaps the most straightforward tactic for improving people's perceptions and attitudes about safety and therefore their long-term participation in safety-related activities. Even our common sense tells us that how people talk about something influences how both the sender and receiver of the communication feel about it. Also, it's intuitive that words like "mandate," "accident," "investigation," "compliance," "behavior modification," "loss control" and even "peer pressure" can be a turnoff to involvement.

More positive "turn-on" language is available, as detailed in Chapter 5, but even this simple change will not come easily. In other words, this recommendation is easier said than done. People develop the mindless habit of using certain language, and need corrective feedback. But before such feedback can work, people need to believe a habit is worth changing. Have I convinced you—the choir—we need to change how we talk about safety?

I'm referring to the words we use when talking to ourselves as well as to others. As covered in Chapter 5, our self-talk and accompanying imagery has dramatic impact on our attitudes, our behaviors, and the way we talk to others. In fact, before we can eliminate a bad habit, we need to use self-talk to become aware of the automatic movements of that habit (Watson and Tharp 1997). We can also use self-conversation to put us in a good or bad mood, and thereby affect our willingness to actively care for the safety of others. As illustrated on the next page, our intrapersonal communication can ruin a good thing. Of course, we can also do the opposite. We can turn lemons into lemonade in our heads, which in turn improves our interactions with the real world.

Our inner world affects our outer world, and vice versa.

2. Shift Safety from Priority to Value

Here's another change in language you need to consider. Calling safety the "Number 1 Priority" puts management in an awkward position. Employees know safety is not number one—profit is. If the company does not make money, there are no jobs, and there's no need for safety. So stop putting safety in a position that competes with profit-making. Instead, give safety a separate and special category—value.

Human values don't change. They define a person's principles or personal standards, like honesty, democracy, courage, and freedom. Core values are never questioned—never compromised. They exist on a higher, more noble plane than priorities. Our vision should be to make safety a value linked with every activity or priority in a work culture. This can happen when we start talking about safety as inherent in every job. Safety is not an extra or separate aspect of a job. It is essential and is integrated into every component of the operation. Being competent, talented, or skilled at something includes doing it safely. At-risk means incompetent. Talk this way about safety to yourself and to others.

3. Take Advantage of the Competence Motive

Let's stop talking about safety as if it's altruistic or self-sacrificing. This gives people an excuse for compromising safe operating procedures. "I just didn't have time to follow all of the precautions this time. I'll do that extra safety stuff next time when I'm not so stressed." This kind of commentary would be less likely if avoiding a safety-related procedure was considered incompetent.

People want to be judged competent. That's the competence motive. Thus, if safety is a value—intrinsic to every job—disregarding any relevant safety process means the job was done incorrectly. The operator was consciously or unconsciously incompetent. Competence can be improved only through feedback, and how to do this was a theme of Chapter 6.

4. Provide Behavior-Focused Feedback

Practice does not make perfect. Only with appropriate feedback can we improve. The key to improving performance through feedback is to be behavior-focused, both in diagnosing a problem and in suggesting ways to improve. Behavioral feedback is objective and impersonal. It merely displays a specific discrepancy between ideal and observed behavior (Geller 2000a). In addition, behavioral feedback can include specific directions on how to reduce a behavioral discrepancy.

When feedback points out a behavioral discrepancy, it is essentially motivational, informing participants how much improvement is needed. For optimal results, this kind of behavioral feedback should come as soon after the relevant behavior as possible. On the other hand, feedback intended to be more instructional than motivational is most influential when it occurs just prior to an opportunity to perform the behavior. In this case, you need to note the corrective action needed to make a certain behavior safer, and then offer behavior-focused instruction when an occasion arises for the target behavior to occur again.

In the workplace, competence-improving feedback can be delivered in three basic ways: 1) through one-on-one coaching conversations, as discussed in Chapter 5; 2) through periodic performance appraisals, as detailed in Chapter 6; and 3) through group data graphs that display a work team's level of specific performance, sometimes as it compares with that of another work team (Geller 2001d; Williams and Geller 2000). Whatever the method for providing feedback—instructional and/or motivational—the context must be positive.

I've heard several behavior-based safety consultants discuss feedback as if it's naturally accepted and used. They imply that involving employees in the development of a behavioral checklist and the posting of behavior-related numbers are all that's needed to put an effective feedback process in place. It's as if people naturally look forward to receiving feedback about their performance.

How do *you* feel when someone asks, "Can I give you some feedback?" Do you really expect a positive experience? Most people do not expect to enjoy a feedback session. Based on a lifetime of experience, people more often link feedback with reprimand than praise. So don't expect people to naturally accept and look forward to receiving behavioral feedback.

The context of a feedback conversation is crucial. The nature of the conversation or group discussion surrounding a feedback session will determine whether or not such a process will be appreciated, supported, and sustained. Therefore, the first feedback session really needs to be positive and constructive. Realize that many people will not look forward to their initial feedback meeting, because they expect to be corrected, perhaps even criticized.

5. Help People Feel Important

This fuel for *The Participation Factor* relates directly to my prior point about the feedback context. Negative feedback can belittle one's sense of importance, and that's disastrous for voluntary participation. That's why it's so important to emphasize a person's positive contributions to worthwhile work—the "Spirit of the Squirrel." When people believe their work is genuinely appreciated, they want to improve. When they become competent at a valuable job, their sense of personal importance increases. Thus, in the spirit of increasing their competence at a valuable work process they are already skilled at performing, people will accept and apply relevant corrective feedback.

6. Help Conversation Progress from Past to Future to Present

As detailed in Chapter 5, conversation is a necessary support for safety, from giving interpersonal recognition and feedback to inspiring work teams with a personal testimony about a safety-related incident. Interpersonal conversation is key to cultivating an ideal interdependent culture in which people actively care for each other's safety and health. Imagine a situation that requires interpersonal cooperation but where interpersonal conversation is difficult or impossible, as illustrated on the next page. The result: potential for frustration, conflict, and the kind of destructive behavior we see in road rage.

When we have opportunities to talk personally with others, we need to move the communication from past to future and then to the present. Conversations about past experiences are pleasant and functional. They define mutual interests, attitudes, or experiences and enable recognition for prior accomplishments, thereby helping people feel important. But if you want productive change from a conversation, don't allow it to get stuck in the past.

*Interpersonal
cooperation
without
opportunities
for interpersonal
conversation
can be
frustrating.*

Whether addressing a team or conducting a performance appraisal, move your communication from the past to a consideration of future possibilities or ideal improvement. Then, after pondering aloud what could be, bring the talk back to the present. Discuss things that can be put into effect now to bring the ideal future a step closer. In other words, follow the next principle about goal setting.

7. Set SMART and SMARTS Goals

Competence improvement and productive results from team meetings and performance appraisals start with goal setting. In other words, a conversation about progress can lead to beneficial change if SMART goals are set. The letters of SMART represent the essential components of an effective goal. As detailed in Chapter 6, a SMART goal is Specific, Motivational, Attainable, Relevant, and Trackable.

Goals for teams are SMARTS, with the added "S" referring to "Shared." Obviously team members need to share the responsibility of reaching a team goal. Elsewhere I explain how to use consensus-building exercises to get team buy-in and a shared commitment for a SMARTS goal (Geller 2001c).

8. Distinguish Goals from Purpose

Literally thousands of studies have demonstrated the power of SMART goals to improve performance at individual, group, organizational, and community levels. When goals are not SMART, they are ineffective. Thus, we set a poor example when we refer to goals that are not SMART. In safety, this happens whenever we say, "Zero injuries is our goal." This is not SMART; it misuses and abuses goal setting.

Please talk about zero injuries as a purpose or vision. Throughout this book I have referred to "an injury-free workplace" as the ultimate result of gaining and sustaining maximum employee involvement in safety-related activities. So our purpose for fueling *The Participation Factor* is to reach and maintain zero injuries. The actual participation is for various process activities that contribute to injury prevention and the attainment of our vision. These process activities can be defined in terms of a certain number of specific actions that need to occur in a given period of time in order to be "successful."

Thus, it's possible to set SMART goals for process activities. These activities and their associated goals change continuously, but the vision of "zero injuries" remains the same. That's what Dr. Deming meant when he referred to "constancy of purpose," the first of his famous fourteen points for the transformation of American industry to improved quality and productivity and lower costs (Deming 1986).

9. Elevate Self- and Response-Efficacy

SMART goals include these two critical ingredients of empowerment, as explained in Chapter 2. Specifically, self-efficacy refers to one's belief that she or he can handle an assignment. Having response-efficacy means the person believes an assignment is useful in accomplishing a particular objective or purpose. Thus, the "attainable" quality of a SMART goal accounts for self-efficacy, while the "relevant" feature relates directly to response-efficacy.

These two belief states have applications and ramifications beyond goal setting. As I described in Chapter 2, for example, both of these belief states need to be addressed and elevated for training to be most effective and for scare tactics to motivate appropriate behavior or attitude change. Actually, whenever you want to persuade an individual or group to participate in a certain activity, you need to develop sufficient self- and response-efficacy.

How much efficacy is enough? Only the recipients of the assignment can adequately answer this critical question. So ask, "Do you believe you can do this?" and "Do you believe this assignment is relevant to our mission statement?" A "no" to either of these questions requires the open-ended question, "What would it take to elevate your belief state?"

10. Sell Outcome-Expectancy

A discussion of self- and response-efficacy connects logically with a consideration of outcome-expectancy. This is the "motivational" component of SMART goals. Specifically, outcome-expectancy means the participant believes the completion of a given activity or the attainment of a certain goal will result in worthwhile consequences. In other words, the performer believes the effect of participating will be worth the effort.

This could be the most difficult and important challenge in getting more involvement in occupational safety. You could convince potential participants they can accomplish a particular safety process (self-efficacy) and that the process can prevent injuries (response-efficacy), but they might still be unmotivated because the consequence of reducing injuries beyond an already low occurrence rate doesn't seem important enough to justify the extra time and inconvenience. After all, none of the potential participants has been seriously hurt without this new safety process.

Increasing outcome-expectancy for safety activities requires your best sales pitch. How should you approach this? Should you attempt to frighten your audience into participating? As I explained in Chapter 2, scare tactics won't work unless the fear emotion is aroused. But we don't get very emotional about the typical presentation of injury statistics.

You could appeal to the audience's altruistic or actively caring spirit by using individual case studies to clarify that some people at this plant have been hurt and without the involvement of the people in the audience, more will suffer personal injury. In other words, you could say something like, "On an individual basis, the probability of injury from a particular at-risk behavior is miniscule, but from a company-wide perspective, the probability of injury is certain without large-scale participation in this safety process." This approach has potential in some settings. But you know what works even better to sell outcome-expectancy—the next strategy for fueling *The Participation Factor*.

11. Encourage Personal Testimonies

I referred specifically to this type of conversation back in Chapter 1 (remember the bottom-line lesson from "The Blue Book Story"). Plus I've used personal testimonies throughout this book to teach and provoke. Did my stories hold your interest more than the standard textbook prose? Could you relate to some of my anecdotes, and in some cases see yourself in a similar situation? Could you create a mental image from the story? In some cases I provided illustrations to facilitate such imagery. Did the visual or mental pictures help you remember the anecdote and the relevant lesson?

Of course, all of these questions are rhetorical—designed to sell the powerful influence of personal testimony. But you probably didn't need any convincing on this. Right! You've been there. You've been influenced by case studies, and you've used the same approach to persuade others. You're sold. Yet the challenge remains. How do we get these kinds of conversations to occur? Well, one thing is certain. It won't happen without solid influence from the next principle.

12. Build Ownership and Interpersonal Trust

People will open up and speak frankly when they take part in developing procedures and trust that those in charge of the process are well-intentioned and capable, as delineated in Chapter 8. The situation depicted below is exactly opposite of what we want. "Of course," you say, "but employees aren't monkeys in a cage who need a lawyer to negotiate on their behalf." But wait a minute. Aren't there some work cultures where employees receive their entire assignment from someone else, do as they're told, and file a grievance if they perceive serious friction or disagreement with a supervisor? Then they rely on the negotiation skills of another individual, tantamount to a lawyer, to handle the conflict. These workers might feel like monkeys in a cage, except

Some work cultures can feel pretty restrictive.

they can look forward to the end of the workday when they punch out and resume a life with opportunities for choice, personal control, and the pleasure of feeling empowered.

This kind of command-and-control work culture is not the norm anymore, except when it comes to safety. For many work cultures, the intrusive role of government in safety issues influences a disconnection between a company's safety and production missions. The result: a mindset that says, "We follow safety regulations for someone else—OSHA—but we manufacture a quality product for our company and our profits." Chapter 8 offers a number of strategies for elevating the level of buy-in and interpersonal trust for the safety mission of an organization. In this regard, the next two strategies for fueling *The Participation Factor* are clearly relevant.

13. Teach Theory and Principles Before Procedures

Many scholars have written about the need to have a guiding theory or set of principles to consult when designing and refining methods and procedures (e.g., Covey 1990; Deming 1993). In fact, by boiling down the right theory or principles into a mission statement, you have created a standard for judging the value of your company's procedures, policies, and performance expectations. You also have a rationale for specific procedures taught during training.

When it comes to safety, many companies start with teaching step-by-step procedures (referred to as "training"). They don't educate people first about the principles or rationale behind a particular safety policy, program, or process. As a result, many safety programs are referred to as "flavor-of-the month." Such hand-me-down programs usually attract less than desired involvement, and they don't last very long.

When people are educated about the principles and rationale behind a safety process, they can customize specific procedures for their own work areas. Then the relevance of the training process is obvious, and participation is enhanced. People are more likely to accept and follow procedures they helped to develop. They see such safe operating procedures as "the best way to do it" rather than "a policy we must obey because management says so."

14. Provide Guidance for Customizing a Process

This principle follows logically from the prior recommendation, but actually runs counter to common practice. So many safety efforts start as off-the-shelf programs. A videotape is shown and ready-made workbooks are followed to teach step-by-step procedures. Much more involvement occurs when consultants begin a new safety effort by first teaching rationale and principles and then guiding participants through the development of specific procedures. Then people will want to be trained on *their own* implementation procedures.

When effective leaders guide the customization of a process, they state expectations, but they don't give mandates or directions. They show both confidence and uncertainty (Geller 2000c; Langer 1989, 1997). In other words, they are confident a set of procedures will be developed, but they don't know the best way to do it. This allows employees room to be alert, innovative, and self-motivated. The result: ownership and interpersonal trust increase, which in turn leads to more involvement.

15. Cultivate Self-Persuasion and Self-Accountability

Choice, ownership, and interpersonal trust contribute to the development of self-persuasion and self-accountability—critically important mindsets for the maintenance of an injury-free workplace. Take a look at the worker illustrated below. There is no one around to hold him accountable for wearing his hard hat. It's hot and he feels safe without the hard hat on his head. Whether or not he wears his hard hat depends entirely on his mental script about hard-hat use. He might say something like, "There's no one around to enforce the dumb

When a worker is alone, self-talk determines whether a safety rule is followed.

hard-hat rule, so here's my opportunity to beat the system." That's an other-directed perspective. He is not self-directed or self-persuaded to use this personal protective equipment.

A self-accountable person might say something like, "I need to wear my hard hat because it's the right thing to do for safety, even though I really don't feel this protective device is needed. It's important for me to develop a regular routine of wearing this hard hat. Safety is part of being skillful and proficient at my job, and consistently wearing this hard hat adds to my competence."

The second, self-accountable, mental script is obviously much preferred over the first. Many factors influence which type of self-talk is more likely in a certain situation, including personality and historical variables beyond the influence of the work culture. But, as discussed in Chapter 4, characteristics of the work site play a major role in determining whether employees are self-directed or other-directed regarding their adherence to various safety rules and their participation in proactive activities designed to prevent injuries.

Research has shown that the more external justification a person feels for a certain activity, the less the internal justification or self-persuasion. Therefore, severe threats and large incentives are powerful motivators only when negative consequences for noncompliance or positive consequences for compliance are available. These conditions inhibit the development of self-persuasion. Therefore, when the motivating consequences cannot be delivered, soon and certain natural consequences take control. This is often not good for safety, since safe behavior usually takes more effort and is less efficient than the at-risk alternative. In other words, the soon and certain natural consequences are most often more positive and less negative for at-risk than safe behavior.

Besides the size of threats and promises, other aspects of a work culture determine whether safety-related participation is other-directed or self-directed. The good news is that many of these factors can be changed to increase the probability of self-persuasion and self-direction. Indeed, how to make this happen is a primary theme of this book, and most of the principles in this chapter relate directly to this challenge.

16. Find Facts Rather than Faults

In Chapter 5, I discussed how the language we use influences attitudes and behavior. Then I specified words frequently used in safety that are detrimental to *The Participation Factor*. "Accident investigation" is a prime example, because it implies fault-finding over fact-finding. To most people an investigation means a search for some single cause or person to blame for a particular incident. As a result, it's logical to conduct a "root cause analysis" and look for one basic fault.

This root cause approach stifles the open conversation needed between people to analyze the situation completely. It can create a narrow, failure-oriented perspective with regard to incident analysis and injury prevention. People don't want to talk about failure, especially if they suspect the finger of blame could point at them. Besides, there is usually no single root cause of an incident, and the cause of an event cannot be discovered by merely talking about potential causative factors.

17. Diagnose Carefully before Intervening

This principle follows logically from the previous one. The purpose of fact-finding is to define the most appropriate corrective action plan. Safety engineers understand this, and are quite competent at dealing with environmental fixes. However, when it comes to addressing the behavioral and person-based factors of the Safety Triad introduced in Chapter 1 (see Figure 1.1), incompetence is common. This is obvious from the numerous corrective action plans I've read on incidence reports.

The environmental aspects of a corrective action plan are often detailed, and they vary considerably as a function of the context of the incident. However, the human dynamics of a proposed safety intervention are usually disappointingly simple and similar. Specifically, the most frequent recommendations addressing the people aspects of corrective action are "The employee will be re-trained" and "The employee will be disciplined." These should actually be last resort interventions, not common recommendations.

As I detail elsewhere (Geller 2000a, 2001d), a proper analysis of the human dynamics of an incident requires a search for answers to the following successive questions:

- What is the discrepancy between observed and ideal participation?
- Is change called for?
- Can the task be simplified?
- Are expectations clear?
- Is performance feedback available?
- What are the natural or intrinsic consequences?
- Is there a skill discrepancy?
- Is the person right for the job?
- What kind of training is needed?
- Which corrective action is most cost-effective?

Note that eight questions need to be answered before training comes into the picture. That's because most participation problems relate to execution rather than aptitude or skill. In other words, workers usually know how to perform a job safely, but might work at-risk for various reasons addressed by the earlier questions in the list. Thus, you need to take the time to find the facts and interpret them carefully before planning a safety intervention. This approach is facilitated when the next principle is adopted and disseminated throughout a work culture.

18. Teach and Promote Systems Thinking

Systems thinkers diagnose with care and certainly don't look for a root cause. They get a broad picture of the situation and consider the dynamic and reciprocal interaction among the three sides of the Safety Triad. For example, changes in an environmental factor affect behaviors and attitudes. And a behavior change usually results in some change in the environment.

When people choose to change their behavior, they adjust their attitudes and beliefs to be consistent with their actions, as explained in Chapter 4. This change in attitude can influence more behavior change and then more attitude change—a spiraling, reciprocal interdependency between our outward actions and our inward feelings. Also, an initial change in behavior and attitude can be sparked by an environmental factor.

Teaching this basic concept, consistent with the scholarship of such continuous-improvement gurus as Drs. Stephen Covey (1989), Edwards Deming (1986), and Peter Senge (1990), can increase people's involvement in all aspects of occupational safety—from analyzing incidents to implementing corrective action plans. Such thinking helps people realize their importance in solving problems without fear of being blamed as a "root cause." It advances understanding of factors outside and inside people that influence participation, thereby providing direction for beneficial self-management (Geller and Clarke 1999). Systems thinkers also see the fallacy in using injury rate as a measure of safety performance, and realize that injury prevention requires a focus on proactive activities upstream from an injury.

19. Use Process Measures of Safety Performance

Both the quantity and quality of participation in safety-related activities depend on the numbers you use to evaluate success or failure. The bottom-line measure—total recordable injury rate (TRIR)—provides neither instructive guidance nor motivation to continue a particular safety process. It tells us nothing about why we're succeeding or failing (O'Brien 2000). Yet companies are frequently ranked according to their OSHA recordables and lost-time injuries. And within organizations, individuals or work teams frequently earn financial bonuses according to outcomes. As discussed in Chapter 1, this motivates employees to cover up their injuries and stifles the very kinds of conversation needed to prevent injuries.

Instead, keep score on the various proactive things individuals and groups do for safety. For example, track the number of corrective actions implemented and evaluated, the number of environmental and behavioral audits conducted, the number of environmental hazards eliminated, the number of safety suggestions and safety work orders submitted, and so on. Graph and post the percentage of individuals who participate in various safety-related activities as well as the percentage of safe work environments and behaviors observed during systematic audits. Now you have an accountability system that can facilitate participation.

20. Hold People Accountable for Numbers They Can Control

Implementing a process-focused accountability system will probably cause some stress in a work force. This kind of measurement system puts pressure on people to do something. As you've heard many times before, "What gets measured gets done." Please note, however, that stress is not bad. As defined in *The American Heritage Dictionary* (1991), "stress [is] importance, significance, or emphasis placed on something" (p. 1205). The bad state is *dis*tress, defined as "anxiety or suffering . . . severe strain resulting from exhaustion or an accident" (*The American Heritage Dictionary* 1991, p. 410).

Holding people accountable for numbers they do not believe they can personally control causes *distress*. This happens every time a graph of injury rates is displayed to a work group as a measure of their safety performance along with the implication that they should try harder. The most direct thing employees can do to improve this statistic is to avoid reporting an injury. In other words, they can cheat to gain some perceived control and thus transform distress to stress.

A far better way to get people involved in participating to reduce industrial injuries is to hold them accountable for accomplishing proactive activities that can prevent a workplace injury. Such an accountability system will engender more participation. To improve the *quality* of the participation, however, you need to apply the next principle.

21. Deliver Quality Recognition

In Chapter 5, I described how to give quality one-to-one recognition. It needs to be given privately, not publicly as advocated by many pop psychologists and motivational speakers. Remember that many people feel embarrassed when receiving special attention in a group context. Part of this discomfort is due to fear of subsequent harassment by peers. They might expect to hear something like, "Why did you get that special recognition about your safe work practices? Have you been kissing up to management again?"

When delivered correctly, positive recognition for safe behavior provides direction and motivation to continue that behavior and improves one's personal attitude toward safety in general. But to fuel *The Participation Factor*, we need to get more people involved in giving positive recognition for quality participation in occupational safety.

Your first challenge might be to convince people that recognition is needed. There seems to be a myth that people can get too much recognition. I'm sure you've heard the expression illustrated below—that too much recognition can give a person a "big head." Well, guess what? A big head is good. The more recognition people receive, the better they feel about themselves; and the better people feel about themselves, the more they will actively care for the safety of others.

When I ask my audiences whether they get enough recognition for the good things they do, few if any individuals raise their hands. But when I ask whether they get enough criticism for the mistakes they make, almost every-

Some people presume that too much recognition is detrimental.

one raises a hand. Then I rest my case. It's obvious we can all use more quality recognition to support and improve our participation for occupational safety.

Obviously, people need to learn how to recognize others appropriately. Sessions that teach the principles of recognizing people well should include role-playing exercises in which participants practice giving behavior-based recognition to another person and then receive behavior-based feedback on their performance. The use of small rewards or "actively caring thank you cards" (Boyce and Geller 2001; Geller 2001d) can be helpful in breaking the ice and initiating a positive approach to promoting safety-related behavior.

22. Receive Recognition Well

As important as it is to give positive recognition correctly, it may be even more important to receive recognition well. That is, the reaction of a person receiving recognition determines whether people become more or less involved in using positive consequences to instruct and motivate safety-related participation. In Chapter 5, I explained the following guidelines for receiving recognition:

- Avoid denials and disclaimers
- Actively listen with sincere appreciation
- Relive the recognition later
- Reward the recognition process
- Embrace the reciprocity principle
- Ask for recognition when it's deserved

23. Celebrate Process and Outcome Success

Celebrations, when done correctly, can be an antidote for sagging morale. They can motivate teamwork, build a sense of belonging, and boost our desire to participate for the safety and health of others. The key is the phrase "when done correctly." Here are some guidelines for conducting quality safety celebrations.

Don't Celebrate Cheating. It's quite common for companies to give employees a dinner after a particular number of weeks or months pass with no recordable injury. This kind of achievement is certainly worth celebrating, but let's be sure the record was reached fairly. If people cheat to win—by not reporting injuries, for example—the celebration won't mean much.

I suggest celebrating the success of process activities. The participation needed to warrant a celebration can be specified. For example, a group might decide to celebrate after completing a designated number of safety audits, investigating a given number of near-hit reports, finishing a particular training series, or completing a certain number of one-on-one safety coaching sessions. In these cases, a SMARTS goal is set and progress is monitored. Then everyone can see when the goal is reached and a celebration is earned.

Focus on the Journey. Most of the safety celebrations I've seen give far too little attention to the journey—the processes that contributed to reaching the milestone. Typically, the focus is on the end result, like achieving zero injuries for a certain period of time. When you pinpoint processes instrumental to reaching a safety milestone, you give valuable direction and motivation. Participants learn what they need to do to continue a successful journey.

Focusing on the journey enables participants to feel responsible for the ultimate outcome of injury reduction. They feel competent, in control, and optimistic. This reinforces their internal self-talk for later self-motivation. But perhaps the most important reason for acknowledging process participation is that it gives credit where credit is due. The people and the participation that made the difference are endorsed.

Recipients Should be Participants. Speeches from top management often kick off safety celebrations. There might be charts comparing past and present records. Sometimes a motivational speaker or humorist gives everyone a lift and some laughs. Certificates and trinkets might be handed out. But rarely do participants discuss the processes they supported in order to achieve success.

In a typical safety celebration, management gives and employees receive —an impressive display of top-down support. However, the ceremony would be more memorable and beneficial as a learning and motivational experience if the employees played a bigger role. Management should listen more than speak. And line workers should talk more about their participation than they listen to managers' pleasure with the bottom line.

Relive the Participation. Management's primary role in a safety celebration should be to facilitate discussions of the activities that led to success. The best safety celebration I ever observed was planned by employees and featured a series of brief presentations by teams of hourly workers. Numerous safety ideas were shared. Some workers showed off new personal protective equipment, some displayed graphs of data obtained from environmental or behavioral audits, some discussed their procedures for encouraging near-hit reports and implementing corrective action, and one group presented its ergonomic analysis and redesign of a work station.

Even the after-dinner entertainment was employee-driven. A skit targeted safety issues. A talent show had entrants from all levels of the organization, including top management. There was no need to hire a band—a number of talented musicians were found in the work force of 1200. (Luckily they didn't find a drummer, so I was able to participate and relive my rock-and-roll gigs of the 1960s.)

Don't Ignore Failures. The work teams in this celebration discussed both successes and failures, displaying the positive results and recalling disappointments, dead ends, and frustrations. Pointing out the highs and lows made their presentations realistic and underscored the amount of involvement needed to complete their projects and contribute to the celebrated reduction in injuries.

You justify a celebration by showing how difficult it was to reach the milestone. Pointing out hardships along the way reflects the fact that luck was not involved. Many people went beyond their normal routines to participate and collaborate.

Make It Memorable. One week after the safety celebration I've described here, each participant received a framed photograph of everyone who attended the event. That picture hangs in my office today, and every time I look at it I'm reminded of the time several years ago when management did more listening than talking in a most memorable and educational safety celebration.

Tangible rewards have this effect. They support the memory of an occasion and promote its value. Ideally, mementos should have a safety theme or slogan and be items that can be displayed or used in the workplace—coffee mugs, caps, or shirts, for example. When delivering these keepsakes it should be noted that they were selected "to remind us how we achieved our real reward—fewer injuries on the job."

Go One-on-One. In every group, some individuals take charge and champion the effort, while others sit back and "go with the flow." In fact, some people exert less effort when working with a group than when working alone. Behavioral scientists call this phenomenon "social loafing" (Latané, Williams, and Harkins 1979).

When you recognize the champions of a group effort one-on-one, you let them know you realize the importance of their special leadership. This adds to the motivation received from the group celebration and increases the likelihood of their continued leadership.

24. Teach and Promote Interdependency

One of the key benefits of quality safety celebrations is the support and promotion of interdependency. As discussed at the beginning of this book, an interdependency mindset is key to obtaining the quantity and quality of employee involvement needed to maintain an injury-free workplace. Cultivating this perspective is not easy. People experience situations every day—from home to work and traveling in between—that reflect win/lose independence. As illustrated below, team sports often promote an independent view, for example by recognizing the most valuable player, often to the detriment of optimal team performance.

As the college football season approaches, I'm reminded of how the university with which I've been affiliated for more than thirty years has struggled to build a reputable football program. When I arrived at Virginia Tech in 1969, football was infrequently a topic of conversation among students and faculty. Saturday competitions did draw thousands of loyal fans, but the stadium of forty thousand seats was never filled except when we played our in-state rival —the University of Virginia—and once when we played Alabama.

What a difference today! Everyone seems to talk football daily during football season and at least every week during the off-season. For the past decade, Virginia Tech has been known nationwide for its football team. And also over this period, financial contributions and the number of new applicants

There's no "most valuable player" (MVP) in optimal teamwork.

to the university have grown beyond expectations. The stadium, with a new one-million-dollar turf surface, now holds fifty-three thousand seats, and twenty thousand more are being added for the 2002 season.

Two months before the start of the 2001 football season, tickets were no longer available for any game. What happened? How did our football program rise from nothing to a contender for the national title in 1999 with an undefeated season, only one loss in 2000 (to the University of Miami), and high expectations for 2001 and beyond?

Obviously, there's no root cause. Many factors contributed to such dramatic improvement, but I'm convinced one factor is paramount. After several losing seasons, the head coach, Frank Beamer, led a transition from independency to interdependency. "Showboating" at the end of a play was outlawed. During interviews, coaches and players began focusing on the special teamwork and synergy that enables success. Players who received media attention for their spectacular plays emphasized the critical roles of other team members. It's now common to hear statements like, "Without the protection of the offensive line and the downfield blocking, I would not have been able to rush for that many yards."

A spirit of win/win interdependence improves the success of teams on the athletic field and on the shop floor. Interdependency is vital to meet the challenge of attaining and sustaining an injury-free workplace. When people understand interdependency, they realize their safety-related behaviors influence the safety of others. They participate in a safety process because they don't want anyone to get hurt, and they realize their good example contributes interdependently to the vision of an injury-free workplace. They also appreciate the role of certain person states in influencing people's willingness to actively care interdependently for the safety of others. This critically important fuel for *The Participation Factor* is explained next.

25. Enhance the Actively Caring Person States

Several years ago, I defined a Total Safety Culture as one in which "everyone feels responsible for safety and pursues it on a daily basis; employees go beyond the call of duty to identify unsafe conditions and behaviors and intervene to correct them . . . [and] people 'actively care' on a continuous basis for safety" (Geller 1994, p. 18).

There is significant overlap between feeling responsible for safety and actively caring for the safety of others. In fact, people who accept personal responsibility for safety are usually willing to go beyond their normal routines for another person's safety and health. Whether such "actively caring" actually occurs, however, depends in part on the individual's psychological state when an opportunity to help someone occurs.

More specifically, research has shown that five person states influence people's willingness to help others: *self-esteem* ("I am valuable"), *belonging* ("I belong to a team"), *self-efficacy* ("I can do it"), *personal control* ("I am in control"), and *optimism* ("I expect the best"). The latter three states influence perceptions of empowerment ("I can make a difference"), along with perceptions of response-efficacy and outcome-expectancy. The statements in quotation marks define the essential meaning of each person state.

These critical actively caring person states are discussed in much more detail in other publications, which also include strategies for increasing them throughout a work culture (Geller 1998b, 2001a, d; Geller and Williams 2001). Plus, as the strategies presented in this book increase involvement in a safety-related process, they also enhance the actively caring person states.

Figure 9.1 depicts this person-based perspective of actively caring. It's a model my associates and I have used for more than a decade to stimulate discussions among industry employees about specific situations, operations, or incidents that influence their willingness to participate actively in safety achievement efforts.

Factors consistently listed as determinants of self-esteem include communication strategies, reinforcement and punishment contingencies, and leadership styles. Participants have suggested a number of ways to build self-esteem, including a) providing opportunities for personal learning and peer mentoring, b) increasing recognition for desirable behaviors and personal accomplishments, and c) soliciting and following up on a person's suggestion.

Figure 9.1 The actively caring model for occupational safety.

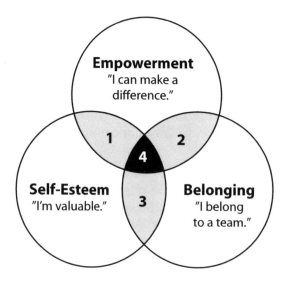

1. I can make valuable differences.
2. We can make a difference.
3. I'm a valuable team member.
4. We can make valuable differences.

Common proposals for increasing an atmosphere of belonging among employees have included decreasing the frequency of top-down directives and "quick fix" programs and increasing team-building discussions, group goal setting and feedback, group celebrations for both process and outcome achievements, and the use of self-managed (or self-directed) work teams.

Empowerment was the theme of Chapter 2, and there I presented a number of tactics for elevating the five belief states that influence empowerment —self-efficacy, response-efficacy, outcome-expectancy, personal control, and optimism. Employees at my behavioral safety training sessions have listed a number of ways to increase empowerment, including a) setting short-term goals and tracking achievements; b) offering frequent rewarding and correcting feedback for process activities rather than only for outcomes; c) providing opportunities to set personal goals, teach peers, and chart "small wins" (Weick 1984); d) teaching employees basic behavior-change intervention strategies such as techniques to give and receive feedback and recognition; e) providing employees time and resources to implement and evaluate intervention programs; f) showing employees how to graph daily records of baseline, intervention, and follow-up data; and g) posting response feedback graphs of group performance.

26. Use Punishment as a Last Resort

There's probably no faster way to depreciate an actively caring mindset than to use punishment—giving an individual a negative consequence for working at-risk or for not following a designated safety procedure. In industry this "behavior modification" technique is unfortunately called "discipline." I say "unfortunately" because my dictionary defines "discipline" as "training that is expected to produce a specific character or pattern of behavior, especially training that produces moral or mental improvement" (*The American Heritage Dictionary*, 1991, p. 402). As I explained in Chapter 1, punishment is essentially ineffective at producing long-term participation, and it can turn individuals and an entire work culture against those doing the punishing.

Use punishment as a last resort—only after you've tried the many other more positive and effective techniques described in this book. Therefore, when you use punishment you've essentially given up on a particular individual and prefer that she or he decide to work somewhere else. If you don't take a rotten apple out of the barrel, it will make the other apples rotten.

Please consider carefully the philosophy behind the "positive discipline" process discussed in Chapter 1. Briefly, the purpose of any corrective action technique is to help the person decide to make an adjustment, not to retaliate or show that you mean business. More likely than not, punishment in an industrial setting signifies an unfair or inconsistent administration of a punitive consequence by a person who doesn't care enough to conduct a comprehensive diagnosis and explore constructive ways to improve the situation. It sets a tone opposite to actively caring.

27. Look Beyond the Numbers

Managers focus on the numbers, and in safety that means injury records and compensation costs. When I teach managers a process to increase employee involvement in safety, I inevitably get the question, "What's the ROI (return on investment)?" Managers want to know how much the process will cost and how long it will take for the numbers (for example, total recordable injuries) to improve. This analytical approach to safety is obviously inspired by the popular management principle I mentioned earlier: "You can only manage what you can measure."

Leaders certainly appreciate the need to hold people accountable with numbers, but they also understand you can't measure everything. There are some things you do and ask others to do because you know it's the right thing to do. Leaders believe, for example, it's important to increase the actively caring states throughout a work culture. Yet they don't attempt to measure their success at increasing self-esteem, feelings of empowerment, and a sense of belonging. They do things on a regular basis to inspire these feeling states in others, but they don't worry about measuring their direct impact on these intangibles. They have faith in the research-supported theory that promoting these person states is important. In the same vein, people take vitamin pills regularly even though they don't notice any measurable effects.

Now and then it's a good idea to assess whether certain actions are influencing people's subjective feelings in a desired direction. This can be done informally through personal interviews, unaided by a score card. It's a given that certain interpersonal and group activities are useful. As I explained earlier, genuine one-to-one recognition increases trust and feelings of importance; SMART goal-setting builds feelings of empowerment; and group celebrations facilitate a sense of belonging. You need to perform and support these sorts of activities without expecting to see an immediate change in the numbers of a safety accountability system.

Leaders don't need a monitoring scheme to motivate their attempts to help people feel valuable and part of a worthwhile team effort. This kind of leadership is self-directed and responsible and helps to inspire self-directed responsibility in others.

28. Apply the Six Principles of Social Influence

I devoted an entire chapter to teaching six fundamental social influence principles that affect the quality and quantity of actively caring participation in a given work culture. The illustration below demonstrates one of these principles—conformity. These principles help explain why people act and react in certain ways and adopt particular attitudes. But more than explaining why people think what they think and do what they do, these principles can be applied systematically to change what people think and do.

In Chapter 7, I used a number of everyday situations to illustrate specific applications of each social influence principle: consistency, reciprocity, conformity, ingratiation, authority, and scarcity. Safety applications were also presented, along with a method for determining your own "social influence profile." I hope you will take the survey, graph your profile, and compare it with the average profiles displayed in Chapter 7. Why? Because this will pique your interest in the six principles of social influence, enrich your understanding of these principles, and motivate you to teach others how to use various social influence techniques to benefit *The Participation Factor* of occupational safety.

Our behavior is often influenced by the behavior of others.

29. Use the Hypocrisy Effect

In Chapter 4, I described a powerful influence procedure that applies the social influence principle of consistency. It has not been formally tested in an industrial safety situation, but has been remarkably successful at increasing participation in efforts to increase water conservation, resource recycling, and the use of condoms. The intervention is based on developing feelings of hypocrisy regarding a certain target behavior, and is ready-made for applications to industrial safety. Just follow the four straightforward steps outlined in Figure 4.1. Please let me know your results so I can report them in the next edition of this book.

30. Build and Maintain Momentum

It's quite fitting to end a book on facilitating participation with a discussion of momentum. In fact, to a large extent, this entire book has been about building and maintaining momentum for occupational safety. Let's consider factors relevant to increasing momentum. We can use another sports analogy for intuitive answers to the critical question "How can we build and maintain momentum?"

I think you'll agree from personal experience that three factors are crucial: achievement of the participants, atmosphere of the culture, and attitude of the coaches and team leaders. These three ingredients of momentum start with the letter "A," so they are easy to remember. As you'll see, they are clearly overlapping and interrelated.

Achievement of the Participants. It's obvious that success builds success. Good performance is more likely after a run of successful behaviors than failures. In sports, a succession of winning plays or points scored creates momentum.

Sports psychologists talk about momentum as a gain in psychological power—including confidence, self-efficacy, and personal control—that changes perceptions and attitudes and enhances both mental and physical performance. It all starts with noticing a run of individual or team achievements. So how can we apply this to *The Participation Factor* in occupational safety?

We've got to keep score. We need a system to track small wins in safety that can build momentum. At sporting events, fans constantly check the scoreboard to measure their team's performance. "Knowing the score" creates excitement if our team is performing well, or urgency if performance must improve. This kind of observable and equitable appraisal gives the team feedback. It improves subsequent performance and increases the probability of more success and continued momentum.

To manage safety successfully, we must find ongoing objective and impartial measures of performance that allow us to regularly evaluate our progress and motivate employees to participate in achievement-oriented processes. This is why I have emphasized here the need to:

- Develop upstream process measures such as number of audits completed or percentage of safe behaviors (see Principle 19).

- Set process-oriented goals that are specific, motivational, attainable, relevant, trackable, and shared—SMARTS—(Principles 7 and 8).

- Discuss safety performance in terms of achievement—what people have done for safety and what additional achievement potential is within their domain of control (Principle 20).

- Recognize individuals appropriately for their accomplishments (Principles 21 and 22).

- Celebrate group or team accomplishments regularly (Principle 23).

Atmosphere of the Culture. In sports, it's called the home field advantage. It means having fans available to help initiate or sustain momentum. By packing the stands and cheering loudly, fans create an atmosphere that can motivate the home team to try harder. Remember the "Gift of the Goose."

I hope the relevance to safety is clear. The atmosphere surrounding the process influences continuous participation in a safety-improvement effort. Is the work culture optimistic about the new safety effort, or is the process viewed as another "flavor of the month?" Do the workers trust management to give adequate support to a long-term intervention, or is this just another "quick fix" reaction that will soon be replaced by another "priority"?

Before helping a work team implement a safety-improvement process, my partners at Safety Performance Solutions insist everyone in the work culture learn the principles underlying the process. Everyone in the culture needs to learn the rationale behind the safety process, even those who will not be involved in actual implementation. This helps to provide the right kind of atmosphere (cultural context) to support the process.

When the vision of a work team is shared optimistically with the entire work force, people are likely to buy in and do what it takes to support the mission. When this happens, interpersonal trust and morale build, along with a winning spirit. People don't fear failure but expect to succeed, and this atmosphere fuels more achievement from the process team.

Attitude of Leaders. The coach of an athletic team can make or break momentum. Coaches initiate and support momentum by helping both individuals and the team recognize their accomplishments. This starts with a clear statement of a vision and attainable goals. Then the leader enthusiastically holds individuals and the team accountable for achieving these goals.

A positive coach can even help members of a losing team feel better about themselves and give momentum a chance. The key is to find pockets of excellence to acknowledge, which builds self-confidence and self-efficacy. Then specific corrective feedback will be accepted as key to being more successful and to building more momentum.

It does little good for safety leaders to reprimand individuals or teams for a poor safety record unless they also provide a method people can use to perform better. And the leader must explain and support the improvement method with confidence, commitment, and enthusiasm.

For momentum to build and continue, support means more than providing necessary resources. It means looking for success stories to recognize and celebrate. This helps to develop feelings of achievement among those directly involved (the team) and an optimistic atmosphere from others (the work culture). These are the ingredients for safety momentum. Keep these in place and your momentum will be sustained. Then you can truly expect the best from your efforts to fuel *The Participation Factor* in occupational safety.

Figure 9.2 Three "A" factors build and maintain momentum.

In Conclusion

Figure 9.2 reviews the three key ingredients I've proposed for building and maintaining momentum in a safety-improvement process. They are clearly overlapping and interrelated, and connect to each of the thirty principles reviewed in this chapter.

The achievement of a team needs to be recognized and supported by everyone—team members, leaders, and the culture at large (Principles 21, 22, and 23). Also, the vision, goals, and commitment of a team leader need to be shared, appreciated, and owned by the team members and everyone else who can encourage and applaud team success (Principles 7, 8, and 12). And when team success is celebrated and held in high regard, the atmosphere of the culture is made more conducive to initiating and supporting momentum.

As a result, the factors influencing momentum actually become by-products of that momentum, and if recognized and appreciated, they in turn help to build more momentum. The result: continuous involvement in safety-process activities designed to achieve and maintain an injury-free workplace. This level of involvement for occupational safety also fuels *The Participation Factor* for every other mission of an organization—from keeping employees satisfied and engaged in worthwhile work to sustaining an enviable level of quality production.

References

Allen, J. 1990. *I saw what you did and I know who you are: Bloopers, blunders and success stories on giving and receiving recognition*. Tucker, Ga.: Performance Management Publications.

American Heritage Dictionary. 1991. Second College Edition, New York: Houghton Mifflin Company.

Aronson, E. 1999. The power of self-persuasion. *American Psychologist* 54:875–884.

Aronson, E., and J. M. Carlsmith. 1963. Effect of severity of threat on the valuation of forbidden behavior. *Journal of Abnormal and Social Psychology* 66:584–588.

Aronson, E., C. Fried, and J. Stone. 1991. Overcoming denial and increasing the intention to use condoms through the induction of hypocrisy. *American Journal of Public Health* 81:1636–1638.

Aronson, E., and J. Mills. 1959. The effect of severity of initiation on liking for a group. *Journal of Abnormal and Social Psychology* 59:177–181.

Aronson, E., T. D. Wilson, and R. M. Akert. 1998. *Social psychology*. 3d ed. New York: Addison Wesley Longman, Inc.

Asch, S. E. 1951. Effects of group pressure upon the modification and distortion of judgments. In *Groups, leadership, and men*, pp. 177-90, edited by H. Guetzkow. Pittsburgh, Pa.: Carnegie Press.

Asch, S. E. 1955. Opinions and social pressure. *Scientific American* 193:31–35.

Bandura, A. 1982. Self-efficacy mechanism in human agency. *American Psychologist* 37:122–147.

———. 1997. *Self-efficacy: The exercise of control*. New York: W. H. Freeman and Company.

Baron, R. A. 1995. *Psychology*, 3d ed. Boston: Allyn and Bacon.

———. 1998. *Psychology*, 5th ed. Boston: Allyn and Bacon.

Bem, D. J. 1972. Self-perception theory. In *Advances in experimental social psychology*, Vol. 6 (pp. 1–60), edited by L. Berkowitz. New York: Academic Press.

Berkowitz, L., and L. R. Daniels. 1963. Responsibility and dependency. *Journal of Abnormal and Social Psychology* 66:429–436.

———. 1964. Affecting the salience of the social responsibility norm: Effect of past help on the responses to dependency relationships. *Journal of Abnormal and Social Psychology* 68:275–281.

Betz, N. E., and G. Hackett. 1986. Applications of self-efficacy theory to understanding career choice behavior. *Journal of Social and Clinical Psychology* 4:263–279.

Bird, F. E., Jr., and G. L. Germain. 1987. *Commitment.* Loganville, Ga.: International Loss Control Institute, Inc.

Blanchard, K. 1999, November. *Building gung ho teams: How to turn people power into profits.* Workshop presented at the Hotel Roanoke, Roanoke, Va..

Blanchard, K., and S. Bowles. 1998. *Gung ho! Turn on the people in any organization.* New York: William Morrow and Company, Inc.

Blanchard, K., P. Zigarmi, and D. Zigarmi. 1985. *Leadership and the one minute manager.* New York: William Morrow and Company, Inc.

Boyce, T. E., and E. S. Geller. 2001. Encouraging college students to support proenvironment behavior: Effects of direct versus indirect rewards. *Environment and Behavior* 33:107–125.

Brehm, J. W. 1966. *A theory of psychological reactance.* New York: Academic Press.

———. 1972. *Responses to loss of freedom: A theory of psychological reactance.* New York: General Learning Press.

Buckingham, M., and C. Coffman. 1999. *First, break all the rules: What the world's greatest managers do differently.* New York: Simon & Schuster, Inc.

Carnegie, D. 1936. *How to win friends and influence people*, 1981 ed. New York: Galahad Books.

Carver, C. S., M. F. Scheier, and J. K. Weintraub. 1989. Assessing coping strategies: A theoretically based approach. *Journal of Personality and Social Psychology* 56:267–283.

Cialdini, R. B. 2001. *Influence: Science and practice*, 4th ed. New York: Harper Collins College Publishers.

Cialdini, R. B., J. T. Cacioppo, R. Basset, and J. A. Miller. 1978. Low-ball procedure for producing compliance: Commitment then cost. *Journal of Applied Social Psychology* 15:492–500.

Cialdini, R. B., J. E. Vincent, S. K. Lewis, J. Catalan, D. Wheeler, and B. L. Darby. 1975. Reciprocal concessions procedure for inducing compliance: The door-in-the-face technique. *Journal of Personality and Social Psychology* 1:206–215.

Clark, R. D., III, and L. E. Word. 1974. Where is the apathetic bystander? Situational characteristics of the emergency. *Journal of Personality and Social Psychology* 29:279–287.

Cook, J., and T. Wall. 1980. New work attitude measures of trust, organizational commitment and personal need non-fulfillment. *Journal of Occupational Psychology* 53:39–52.

Conger, J. A., and R. N. Kanungo. 1988. The empowerment process: Integrating theory and practice. *Academy of Management Review* 13:471–482.

Covey, S. R. 1989. *The seven habits of highly effective people: Restoring the character ethic.* New York: Simon and Schuster, Inc.

———. 1990. Principle-centered leadership. New York: Simon and Schuster.

Crutchfield, R. S. 1955. Conformity and character. *American Psychologist* 10:191–198.

Daniels, A. C. 2000. *Bringing out the best in people: How to apply the astonishing power of positive reinforcement*, 2d ed. New York: McGraw-Hill, Inc.

Deming, W. E. 1986. *Out of the crisis.* Cambridge, Mass.: Center for Advanced Engineering Study, Massachusetts Institute of Technology.

————. 1991, May. *Quality, productivity, and competitive position*. Four-day workshop presented in Cincinnati, Ohio by Quality Enhancement Seminars, Inc., Los Angeles, Calif.

————. 1992, January. *Instituting Dr. Deming's methods for management of productivity and quality*. Two-day workshop presented in Washington, D. C. by Quality Enhancement Seminars, Inc.

————. 1993. *The new economics for industry, government, education*. Cambridge, Mass.: Center for Advanced Engineering Study, Massachusetts Institute of Technology.

DePasquale, J. P., and E. S. Geller. 1999. Critical success factors for behavior-based safety: A study of 20 industry-wide applications. *Journal of Safety Research* 30 (4):237–249.

DeYoung, R. 2000. Expanding and evaluating motives for environmentally responsible behavior. *Journal of Social Issues* 56:509–526.

Dickerson, C. A., R. Thibodeau, E. Aronson, and D. Miller. 1992. Using cognitive dissonance to encourage water conservation. *Journal of Applied Social Psychology* 22:841–854.

Drake, J. D. 1997. *Performance appraisal: One more time*. Menlo Park, Calif: Crisp Publications, Inc.

Drebinger Jr., J. W. 1997. *Mastering safety communication*. Galt, Calif: Wulamoc Publishing.

Elder, J. P., E. S. Geller, M. F. Hovell, and J. A. Mayer. 1994. *Motivating health behavior*. New York: Delmar Publishers.

Eskew, R. T., and C. V. Riche. 1982. Pacing and locus of control in quality control inspection. *Human Factors* 24:411–415.

Eysenck, H. J., and M. W. Eysenck. 1985. *Personality and individual differences: A natural science approach*. New York: Plenum Press.

Festinger, L. 1957. *A theory of cognitive dissonance*. Stanford, Calif.: Stanford University Press.

Festinger, L., and J. M. Carlsmith. 1959. Cognitive consequences of forced compliance. *Journal of Abnormal and Social Psychology* 58:203–210.

Foster, R. D. 2000, May. *National Safety Council position/policy request form*. Dallas: U.S. Department of Labor and OSHA.

Frederick, J., and S. Howe. 2001, February. The employee's perspective on behavioral safety. Paper presented at the ASSE Symposium, Behavioral Safety: The Next Step, Orlando, Fla.

Freedman, J. L. 1965. Long-term behavioral effects of cognitive dissonance. *Journal of Experimental and Social Psychology* 1:145–155.

Freedman, J. L., and S. C. Fraser. 1966. Compliance without pressure: The foot-in-the-door technique. *Journal of Personality and Social Psychology* 4:195–203.

Fried, C., and E. Aronson. 1995. Hypocrisy, misattribution, and dissonance reduction: A demonstration of dissonance in the absence of aversive consequences. *Personality and Social Psychology Bulletin* 21:925–933.

Geller, E. S. 1981. Evaluating energy conservation programs: Is verbal report enough? *Journal of Consumer Behavior* 8:331–334.

————. 1988. A behavioral science approach to transportation safety. *Bulletin of the New York Academy of Medicine* 65:632–661.

————. 1989. Using television to promote safety belt use. In *Public communication campaigns*, 2d ed., edited by R. E. Rice and C. K. Atkins. Newbury Park, Calif.: Sage Publications, Inc.

————. 1994. Ten principles for achieving a Total Safety Culture. *Professional Safety* 39 (9):18–24.

————. 1995. Safety coaching: Key to achieving a Total Safety Culture. *Professional Safety* 40 (7):16–22.

————. 1996. The truth about safety incentives. *Professional Safety* 42 (1):40–44.

————. 1997a. Key processes for continuous safety improvement: Behavior-based recognition and celebration. *Professional Safety* 42 (10):40–44.

————. 1997b. The social dynamics of occupational safety. In *Proceedings of the 36th Annual ASSE Professional Development Conference* (pp. 421–437), New Orleans. Des Plaines, Ill.: American Society of Safety Engineers.

————. 1998a. *Applications of behavior analysis to prevent injury from vehicle crashes,* 2d ed. Monograph published by the Cambridge Center for Behavioral Studies, Cambridge, Mass.

————. 1998b. *Understanding behavior-based safety: Step-by-step methods to improve your workplace,* 2d ed. Neenah, Wis.: J. J. Keller & Associates, Inc.

————. 1999. Behavior-based safety: Confusion, controversy, and clarification. *Occupational Health & Safety* 68 (1):40, 42, 44, 46, 48–49.

————. 2000a. Behavioral safety analysis: A necessary precursor to corrective action. *Professional Safety* 45 (3):29–32.

————. 2000b. Stress versus distress: Implications for occupational safety and health. In *Proceedings of Best Practices in Safety, Health, & Environmental Management for the Complete Safety Manager.* Atlantic City, N.J.: American Society of Safety Engineers.

————. 2000c. Ten leadership qualities for a Total Safety Culture: Safety management is not enough. *Professional Safety* 45 (5):38–41.

————. 2001a. Actively caring for occupational safety: Extending the performance management paradigm. In *Handbook of organizational performance: Behavior analysis and management* (pp. 303–326), edited by C. M. Johnson, W. K. Redmon, and T. C. Mawhinney. New York: The Haworth Press.

————. 2001b. *Beyond safety accountability.* Rockville, Md.: Government Institutes.

————. 2001c. *Building successful safety teams.* Rockville, Md.: Government Institutes.

————. 2001d. *The psychology of safety handbook.* Boca Raton, Fla.: CRC Press.

————. 2001e. What's so special about behavioral safety. *Proceedings of the ASSE Behavioral Safety Symposium: The Next Step* (pp. 11–25), Orlando, Fla.

————. 2001f. Will behavior-based safety reach its potential: Cause for optimism and alarm. In *Keys to behavior-based safety from Safety Performance Solutions* (pp. 415–427), edited by E. S. Geller and J. A. Williams. Rockville, Md.: Government Institutes.

Geller, E. S., and S. W. Clarke. 1999. Safety self-management: A key behavior-based process for injury prevention. *Professional Safety* 44 (7):29–33.

Geller, E. S., J. B. Erickson, and B. A. Buttram. 1983. Attempts to promote residential water conservation with educational, behavioral, and engineering strategies. *Population and Environment* 6:96–112.

Geller, E. S., and G. R. Lehman. 1991. The buckle-up promise card: A versatile intervention for large-scale behavior change. *Journal of Applied Behavior Analysis* 24:91–94.

Geller, E. S., D. S. Roberts, and M. R. Gilmore. 1996. Predicting propensity to actively care for occupational safety. *Journal of Safety Research* 27:1–8.

Geller, E. S., and J. H. Williams, eds. 2001. *Keys to behavior-based safety from Safety Performance Solutions.* Rockville, Md.: ABS Consulting.

Gray, J. 1992. *Men are from Mars, women are from Venus.* New York: Harper Collins.

Grote, D. 1995. *Discipline without punishment.* New York: American Management Association.

Hackett, G., N. E. Betz, J. M. Casas, and I. A. Rocha-Singh. 1992. Gender, ethnicity, and social cognitive factors predicting the academic achievement of students in engineering. *Journal of Counseling Psychology* 39:527–538.

Hale, J. L., and J. P. Dillard. 1995. Fear appeals in health promotion campaigns: Too much, too little, or just right? In *Designing health messages: Approaches from communication theory and public health practice* (pp. 65–80), edited by E. Maibach and R. L. Parrott. Thousand Oaks, Calif.: Sage Publications, Inc.

Hauenstein, N. A. 1992. An information-processing approach to leniency in performance judgments. *Journal of Applied Psychology* 77:485–493.

Hayakawa, S. I. 1978. *Language in thought and action,* 4th ed. New York: Harcourt Brace Jovanovich, Publishers.

Hersey, P., and K. Blanchard. 1982. *Management of organizational behavior,* 4th ed. Englewood Cliffs, N.J.: Prentice Hall.

Horowitz, I. A. 1972. Attitude change as a function of perceived arousal. *Journal of Social Psychology* 87:117–126.

Hovland, C., and W. Weiss. 1951. The influence of source credibility on communication effectiveness. *Public Opinion Quarterly* 15:635–650.

Howe, J. 1998. A union critique of behavioral safety. Presentation at the ASSE Behavioral Safety Symposium, Orlando, Fla.

Hoyle, B. 1998. *Fixing the workplace, not the worker: A workers' guide to accident prevention.* Lakewood, Colo.: Oil, Chemical and Atomic Workers International Union.

Hunt, M. M. 1993. *The story of psychology.* New York: Doubleday.

Isen, A. M., and P. F. Levin. 1972. Effect of feeling good on helping: Cookies and kindness. *Journal of Personality and Social Psychology* 21:384–388.

Judd, C. M., C. N. Ryan, and B. Park. 1991. Accuracy in the judgment of in-group and out-group variability. *Journal of Personality and Social Psychology* 61:745–755.

Kamp, J. 2001. It's time to drag behavioral safety into the cognitive era. *Professional Safety* 46(10):30-34.

Kaplan, S. 2000. Human nature and environmentally responsible behavior. *Journal of Social Issues* 56:491–508.

Kirkpatrick, S. A., and E. A. Locke. 1991. Leadership: Do traits matter? *Academy of Management Executive* 5 (2):48–60.

Krause, T. R., J. H. Hidley, and S. J. Hodson. 1996. *The behavior-based safety process: Managing improvement for an injury-free culture,* 2d ed. New York: Van Nostrand Reinhold.Krisco, K. H. 1997. *Leadership and the art of conversation.* Rocklin, Calif.: Prima Publishing.

Kristiansen, C. M., R. Giulietti. 1990. Perceptions of wife abuse: Effects of gender attitudes toward women, and just-world beliefs among college students. *Psychology of Women Quarterly* 14:177–189.

Langer, E. J. 1989. *Mindfulness*. Reading, Mass.: Addison-Wesley.

———. 1997. *The power of mindful learning*. Reading, Mass.: Perseus Books.

Larson, J. 1996. *Steering clear of highway madness*. Wilsonville, Ore.: Bookpartners, Inc.

———. 1999. *Road rage to road-wise*. New York: Tom Doherty Associates.

Latané, B., J. M. Darley. 1970. *The unresponsible bystander: Why doesn't he help?* New York: Appleton-Century-Crofts.

Latané, B., K. Williams, and S. Harkins. 1979. Many heads make light the work: The causes and consequences of social loafing. *Journal of Personality and Social Psychology* 37:823–832.

Lazarus, R. S. 1980. The stress and coping paradigms. In *Theoretical bases for psychopathology* (pp. 177–214), edited by C. Eisdorfer, D. Cohen, A. Klienmen, and P. Maxim. New York: Spectrum.

Lerner, M. J. 1980. *The belief in a just world: A fundamental delusion*. New York: Plenum.

Leventhal, H., M. A. Shafer, and D. M. Panagis. 1983. The impact of communications on the self-regulation of health beliefs, decision, and behavior. *Health Education Quarterly* 10:3–29.

Ludwig, T. D., and E. S. Geller. 2001. *Intervening to improve the safety of occupational driving: A behavior-change model and review of empirical evidence*. New York: The Haworth Press, Inc.

Manuel, F. 1998. Perspectives on behavioral safety: Observations of ASSE's behavior safety symposium. *Professional Safety* 43 (8):32–37.

Maslow, A. H. 1954. *Motivation and personality*. New York: Harper.

McCaul, K. D., L. G. Veltum, V. Boyechko, and J. J. Crawford. 1990. Understanding attributions of victim blame for rape: Sex, violence, and foreseeability. *Journal of Applied Social Psychology* 20:1–26.

McSween, T. E. 1995. *The value-based safety process: Improving your safety culture with a behavioral approach*. New York: Van Nostrand Reinhold.

Milgram, S. 1963. Behavioral studies of obedience. *Journal of Abnormal and Social Psychology* 67:371–378.

———. 1974. *Obedience to authority*. New York: Harper Collins.

Miller, G. A. 1956. The magical number seven, plus or minus two: Some limits on our capacity to process information. *Psychological Review* 63:81–97.

Mitchell, T. R., S. G. Green, and R. S. Wood. 1982. An attributional model of leadership and the poor performing subordinate: Development and validation. In *Research in organizational behavior*, vol. 3, edited by B. M. Staw and L. L. Cummings. Greenwich, Conn.: JAI Press.

Murphy, K. R., J. N. Cleveland. 1991. *Performance appraisal: An organizational perspective*. Boston: Allyn & Bacon.

Murphy, K. R., R. A. Jako, and R. L. Anhalt. 1993. Nature and consequences of halo error: A critical analysis. *Journal of Applied Psychology* 78:218–225.

Murphy, S. M. 1990. Models of imagery in sport psychology: A review. *Journal of Mental Imagery* 14:153–172.

Myers, I. B., and M. H. McCaulley. 1985. *Manual: A guide to the development and use of the Myers-Briggs Type Indicator.* Palo Alto, Calif.: Consulting Psychologists Press.

National Safety Council. 1998. *Accident facts.* Itasca, Ill.: National Safety Council.

Nemeth, C. 1986. Differential contribution of majority and minority influence. *Psychological Review* 93:23–32.

Nerenberg, A. P. 1995. *The handbook for overcoming road rage: The 10-step compassion program.* Los Angeles: Seed-Thought Publishers.

*New Merriam-Webster.*1989. Springfield, Mass.: Merriam-Webster, Inc., Publishers.

Nowicki, S., and B. R. Strickland. 1973. A locus of control scale for children. *Journal of Consulting Psychology* 40:148–154.

O'Brien, D. P. 2000. *Business measurements for safety performance.* New York: Lewis Publishers.

Peter, L. J. 1969. *The Peter Principle.* New York: Morrow

Peterson, C. 2000. The future of optimism. *American Psychologist* 55 (1):44–55.

Peterson, C., and L. C. Barrett, L. C. 1987. Explanatory style and academic performance among university freshmen. *Journal of Personality and Social Psychology* 53:603–607.

Petersen, D. 1989. *Safe behavior reinforcement.* New York: Aloray, Inc.

———. 2001. *Authentic involvement.* Itasca, Ill.: National Safety Council.

Phares, E. S. 1991. *Introduction to personality,* 3rd ed. New York: Harper Collins.

Piliavin, J. A., J. F. Dovidio, S. L. Gaertner, and R. D. Clark, III. 1981. *Emergency intervention.* New York: Academic Press.

Rees, F. 1997. *Teamwork form start to finish.* San Francisco: Jossey-Bass, Inc.

Robertson, L. S. 1976. The great seat-belt campaign flop. *Journal of Communication* 26:41–46.

Robertson, L. S., A. B. Kelley, B. O'Neill, C. W. Wixom, R. S. Eiswirth, and W. Haddon. 1974. A controlled study of the effect of television messages on safety-belt use. *American Journal of Public Health* 64:1071–1080.

Robbins, T. L., and A. S. DeNisi. 1994. A closer look at interpersonal affect as a distinct influence on cognitive processing in performance evaluations. *Journal of Applied Psychology* 79:341–353.

Rotter, J. B. 1966. Generalized expectancies for internal versus external control of reinforcement. *Psychological Monographs* 80, No. 1.

Rushton, J. P. 1984. The altruistic personality: Evidence from laboratory, naturalistic and self-report perspectives. In *Development and maintenance of prosocial behavior,* edited by E. Staub, D. Bar-Tal, J. Karylowski, and J. Reykowski. New York: Plenum.

Ryan, R. M., and E. L. Deci. 2000. Self-determination theory and the facilitation of intrinsic motivation, social development, and well-being. *American Psychologist* 55:68–78.

Sandman, P. M. 1991. *Risk = hazard + outrage: A formula for effective risk communication.* Videotaped presentation for the American Industrial Hygiene Association, Environmental Communication Research Program, Cook College, Rutgers University, New Brunswick, N.J.

Sarkus, D. J. 2001. Safety and psychology: Where do we go from here? *Professional Safety,* 46 (1):18–25.

Schachter, S., and J. E. Singer. 1962. Cognitive, social, and physiological determinants of emotional state. *Psychological Review* 69:379–399.

Scheier, M. F., and C. S. Carver. 1985. Optimism, coping and health: Assessment and implications of generalized outcome expectancies. *Health Psychology* 4:219–247.

Scheier, M. F., J. K. Weintraub, and C. S. Carver. 1986. Coping with stress: Divergent strategies of optimists and pessimists. *Journal of Personality and Social Psychology* 51:1257–1264.

Seligman, M. E. P. 1991. *Learned optimism.* New York: Alfred A. Knopf.

Selye, H. 1974. Stress without distress. Philadelphia: Lippincott.

Senge, P. M. 1990. *The fifth discipline: The art and practice of the learning organization.* New York: Doubleday/Currency.

Sherer, M., J. E. Maddox, B. Mercandante, S. Prentice-Dunn, B. Jacobs, and R. W. Rogers. 1982. The self-efficacy scale: Construction and validation. *Psychological Reports* 51:663–671.

Shotland, R. L., and W. D. Heinold. 1985. Bystander response to arterial bleeding: Helping skills, the decision-making process, and differentiating the helping response. *Journal of Personality and Social Psychology* 49:347–356.

Simon, S. 2001. Implementing culture change—Three strategies. *Proceedings of the ASSE Behavioral Safety Symposium: The Next Step* (pp. 135–140). Orlando, Fla.

Skinner, B. F. 1953. *Science and human behavior.* New York: Macmillan.

———. 1971. *Beyond freedom and dignity.* New York: Alfred A. Knopf.

———. 1974. *About behaviorism.* New York: Alfred A. Knopf.

Slovic, P. 1991. Beyond numbers: A broader perspective on risk perception and risk communication. In *Deceptable evidence: Science and values in risk management* (pp. 48–65), edited by D. G. Mayo and R. D. Hollander. New York: Oxford University Press.

Strickland, B. R. 1989. Internal-external control expectancies: From contingency to creativity. *American Psychologist* 44:1–12.

Sulzer-Azaroff, B. 1998. *Who killed my daddy? A behavioral safety fable.* Cambridge, Mass.: Cambridge Center for Behavioral Studies.

Sulzer-Azaroff, B., K. B. McCann, and T. C. Harris. 2001. The safe performance approach to preventing job-related illness and injury. In *Handbook of organizational performance: Behavior analysis and management* (pp. 277–302), edited by C. M. Johnson, W. K. Redmon, and T. C. Mawhinney. New York: The Haworth Press.

Summers, G., and N. S. Feldman. 1984. Blaming the victim versus blaming the perpetrator: An attributional analysis of spouse abuse. *Journal of Social and Clinical Psychology* 2:339–347.

Sutton, S. R. 1982. Fear-arousing communications: A critical examination of theory and research. In *Social psychology and behavioral medicine,* edited by J. R. Eiser. London: Wiley.

Tavris, C., and C. Wade. 1995. *Psychology in perspective.* New York: Harper Collins College Publishers.

Taylor, S. E. 1991. *Health psychology,* 2d ed. New York: McGraw-Hill.

Taylor, S. E., L. A. Peplau, and D. O. Sears. 2000. *Social psychology,* 10th ed. Upper Saddle River, N.J.: Prentice Hall.

Topf, M. D. 1998. Behavioral safety: A multifactorial approach. *Professional Safety* 43 (8):34–35.

———. (2001). Behavioral? Holistic? Forget what you call it. Here's what works! *Proceedings of the ASSE Behavioral Safety Symposium: The Next Step* (pp. 85–94). Orlando, Fla.

Triandis, H. C. 1977. *Interpersonal behavior*. Monterey, Calif.: Brooks/Cole.

———. 1985. The self and social behavior in differing cultural contexts. *Journal of Personality and Social Psychology* 96:506–520.

Tuckman, B. W. 1965. Developmental sequence in small groups. *Psychological Bulletin* 63: 384–399.

Tuckman, B. W., and M. A. C. Jensen. 1977. Stages of small group development revisited. *Group and Organizational Studies* 2:419–427.

Valins, S. 1966. Cognitive effects of false heart-rate feedback. *Journal of Personality and Social Psychology* 4:400–408.

Watson, D. C., and R. G. Tharp. 1997. *Self-directed behavior: Self-modification for personal adjustment*, 7th ed. Pacific Grove, Calif.: Brooks/Cole Publishing.

Weick, K. E. 1984. Small wins: Redefining the scale of social problems. *American Psychologist* 39 (1):40–49.

White, R. W. 1959. Motivation reconsidered: The concept of competence. *Psychological Review* 66:297–333.

Williams, J. H., and E. S. Geller. 2000. Behavior-based intervention for occupational safety: Critical impact of social comparison feedback. *Journal of Safety Research* 31 (3):135–142.

Winett, R. A. 1986. *Information and behavior: Systems of influence*. Hillsdale, N.J.: Lawrence Erlbaum Associates.

Witte, K., and M. Allen. 2000. A meta-analysis of fear appeals: Implication for effective public health campaigns. *Health Education & Behavior* 27:591–615.

Yukl, G. 1989. *Leadership in organizations*, 2d ed. Englewood Cliffs, N.J.: Prentice Hall.

Zaccaro, S. J., R. J. Foti, and D. A. Kenny. 1991. Self-monitoring and trait-based variance in leadership: An investigation of leader flexibility across multiple group situations. *Journal of Applied Psychology* 76:308–315.

Index

Words, use of, 88. *See also:* Conversation
    "Behavior analysis"—not "behavior modification", 91
    "Incident analysis"—not "investigation", 89–90
    "Injury"—not "accident", 88–89
    "root cause", 90
    "Safety belt"—not "restraint", 90
    "Value"—not "priority", 90–91
Work culture, 44. *See also:* Culture

Z
Zaccaro, S. J., 172
Zigarmi, D., 172
Zigarmi, P., 172